BIO-MAGNETIC THERAPY

BIO-MAGNETIC THERAPY
HEALING IN YOUR HANDS

BY

SWAMI NIRMALANANDA GIRI
(ABBOT GEORGE BURKE)

LIGHT OF THE SPIRIT
PRESS
CEDAR CREST, NEW MEXICO

Published by
Light of the Spirit Press
lightofthespiritpress.com

Atma Jyoti Ashram (Light of the Spirit Monastery)
P. O. Box 1370
Cedar Crest, New Mexico 87008
OCOY.org

ISBN-13: 978-1-955046-22-0
Library of Congress Control Number: 2023943978

Second Edition 2023

BISAC Categories:

HEA032000	HEALTH & FITNESS / Alternative Therapies
HEA009000	HEALTH & FITNESS / Healing
OCC011000	BODY, MIND & SPIRIT / Healing / General
OCC011010	BODY, MIND & SPIRIT / Healing / Energy (Qigong, Reiki, Polarity)

08172023

CONTENTS

CHAPTER ONE

WHAT IS MAGNETISM AND WHAT IS BIO-MAGNETIC THERAPY?

Two hundred years ago the great healer, Dr. Franz Anton Mesmer, wrote: "All doubts have been removed from my mind that there exists in Nature a universally acting principle which, independently of ourselves, operates–and which we vaguely attribute to Art *and* Nature."

A neatly packaged definition of Magnetism is impossible for two reasons: 1) limitation of study of the question, and 2) limitation of our knowledge of the forces circulating around us in the universe. This much I can tell you: it is a force, a power. And this force/power behaves like both electricity and magnetism, whatever they may really be. Many people have thought it is much more, some even attributing divinity to it, and others have considered it to be much less. Some think it does not exist at all except in the power of suggestion (whatever that is, as well). But most people just do not have any idea about it at all because they have never heard or thought of it.

Historical Views On Magnetism

The great German poet-philosopher, Goethe, said: "Magnetism is a universal active power, which everyone possesses, differing only according to his individuality. Its effects extend to everything and in all cases. The Magnetic power of man reaches out to all mankind, to animals and to plants." The philosopher Schopenhauer was even more firm: "Whoever doubts the fact of healing Magnetism is not only unbelieving but ignorant."

Many inscriptions and figures on ancient Egyptian tablets show definitely that the Egyptians were accustomed to using Magnetism for healing the sick. Among the ancients, Aesculapius was considered the founder of the healing art. And his name is sworn by in the Hippocratic Oath taken by all modern American physicians. Yet we are told by the ancient writings that Aesculapius healed mostly through the application of Magnetism to the suffering. Magnetism was daily practiced in the temples of Isis, Osiris and Serapis. In these temples the priests treated the sick and cured them, mostly with Magnetism imparted in various ways. Mummy cases and talismans, as well as wall paintings, show priests and priestesses treating the sick with varying positions of the hands. All such representations were a mystery only to those unacquainted with Magnetism and its techniques of application.

Celsus, nearly two thousand years ago, was a vigorous advocate of this form of Magnetic treatment, and incidentally proves that it was known and practiced long before his time. Therefore the Flemish philosopher, Von Helmont, wrote:

"Magnetism is active everywhere, and has nothing new but the name: it is a paradox only to those who ridicule whatever they themselves are unable to explain."

In February of 1826, a commission was appointed by the French Government to study the viability of Bio-Magnetic Therapy. For five years the members studied the application and effects of Magnetism and finally drew up their report in 1831. At the end of the document thirty conclusions were enumerated, the twenty-ninth being: "Considered as a cause of certain psychological phenomena, or as a therapeutic remedy, Magnetism ought to be allowed a place within the circle of medical sciences."

A Personal View

My opinion is that what I am calling Magnetism in this book is electricity, magnetism and quite a lot more. Mesmer called it "Animal Magnetism." By "animal" he meant soul (in Latin: *anima*) power, that fundamental life-force which animates all living bodies. Others called it "Vital Magnetism," but really meant the same thing, because "vital" comes from the Latin word *vita*–life.

"And God... breathed upon his face the breath of life, and the man became a living soul" (Genesis 2:7). The word translated "soul" here is *psychin* (psyche), which means much more than spirit. It means the whole living complex of a human being, especially his mind. And since the ruling power of the mind over our bodies has been more than adequately demonstrated by modern psychology in its studies of psychosomatic disease, we can see that this particular term is perfect in expressing the origin of life in man. Modern physics has definitely established that the life which is in man is also in the entire universe. Here, too, the Genesis account has something to say: "And God said, Let there be light, and there was light" (Genesis 1:3), long before the suns lit up the universe (Genesis 1:14-18).

When Paramhansa Yogananda–known to millions through his *Autobiography of a Yogi*–visited the Bavarian stigmatist and miracle-worker, Theresa Neumann, in 1935, he asked her how it was possible for her to have lived for years without food or drink of any kind whatsoever. She replied: "I live by God's light." He commented: "I see you realize that energy flows to your body from the ether, sun, and air." She smiled and said: "I am so happy to know you understand how I live." Putting the biblical account and this modern incident together, we can see that "light" signifies the fundamental life-force in all things, and its various modifications in the varying forms of existence.

"An illuminating experiment was made by Lafontaine with a number of lizards. They were deprived of all food. Two of the lizards were treated by magnetic strokings, the fingers being held just above the skin as they travelled down the body. Those lizards that were not so treated died for want of nourishment, while those two which received the strokings along their bodies outlived the others, one by forty-two days and the other by seventy-five days, still without food" (Leslie O. Korth, *Healing Magnetism*, p. 19).

From my observation it seems evident that what I am calling Magnetism is a single entity, but it has many aspects and manifestations. It is indeed electrical and magnetic; but it is much more. You can put any name to it you like in your working with it, but do put it to work.

"Vital Force is that which underlies all physical action of the body. It is that which causes the circulation of the blood–the movements of the cells–in fact all the motions upon which depend the life of the physical body. Without this Vital Force, there could be no life–no motion–no action. Some call it nervous force, but it is the one thing, no matter by what name it may be called. It is this force that is sent forth from the nervous system by an effort of the will, when we wish a muscle to move....

"Man absorbs his supply of Vital Force from the food he eats; the water he drinks; and largely from the air he breathes.... This Vital Energy is stored up in the Brain, and great nerve centers of the body, from which it is drawn to supply the constantly arising wants of the system. It is distributed over the wires of the nervous system, to all parts of the body. In fact, every nerve is constantly charged with Vital Force, which is replenished when exhausted. Every nerve is a 'live wire,' through which the flow of Vital Force proceeds. And, more than this, every cell in the body, no matter where it is located, or what work it is doing, contains more or less Vital Energy, at all times.

"A strong, healthy person is one who is charged with a goodly supply of Vital Force, which travels to all parts of the body, refreshing, stimulating, and producing activity and energy. Not only does it do this, but it surrounds his body like an aura, and may be felt by those coming in contact. A person depleted of Vital Force will manifest ill-health, lack of vitality, etc., and will only regain his normal condition when he replenishes his store of Vitality." So says William Walker Atkinson writing under the penname of Yogi Ramacharaka.

Magnetism flows throughout the universe, enlivening all things. This is why Mesmer also called it "vital fluid." This force moves invisibly through all existing things. It can flow in basically two ways: harmoniously or inharmoniously; rhythmically or sporadically; freely or obstructed to some degree. When it becomes totally blocked or reduced to below a critical degree the result is death.

So we can say that harmonious, unobstructed flow of this Magnetism is health; inharmonious or obstructed flow of Magnetism is disease. And the cessation of Magnetic flow or its critical reduction results in death. Mesmer put it this way: "Man is in a condition of health when all parts of which he is composed are able to exercise the functions for which they were destined. If perfect order rules all of his functions, one calls this state the state of harmony. Sickness is the opposite state–that is, one wherein harmony is disturbed.... The remedy is that which reestablishes the order or harmony which has been disturbed." And again: "Life in all creatures in the universe is one and the same: it consists of the movement of the most subtle substance. Death is repose, or the cessation of motion. The natural and inevitable course of life consists in passing through the state of fluidity to that of solidity.... Illness is therefore nothing more than a disturbance of the progression of the movement of life."

More modern research has also come to the same conclusions. Sister Justa Smith, enzymologist and chairman of the chemistry department at Rosary Hill College in Buffalo, New York, has been deeply studying the effect of the healing forces emanating from the hands on enzymes. She has established that magnetic fields increase enzyme activity, while ultraviolet light damages it. Not only did Sister Justa find that the enzymes were greatly increased in activity when held in the hands of a magnetically strong person, she also discovered that if she damaged enzymes with ultraviolet light and then had that vial held in the same person's hands for some time, the enzymes would be healed–restored to their normal activity. Further, she also experimented with exposing enzymes to high magnetic fields using regular magnets. She found that the activity of the enzymes in the vial treated by the healer was the same as the vials subjected to a magnetic field of thirteen thousand gauss.

You Are A Magnet

Man himself is a magnet. From the moment of his conception this universal Magnetism begins to flow through his physical entity until its cessation at his death. This reveals another principle: by its presence the *spirit* stimulates this flow we call life, and by its departure that flow ceases. In other words, the spirit causes this flow which in turn causes the life of the body. As God the Universal Spirit causes life in all matter, so the individual spirit causes the microcosm of the body to live and function in the greater universe.

Proof that everything is alive is that everything is *magnetic*. There is nothing in existence that does not have two poles–positive and negative. In testing a piece of string, one end will be found positive and the other negative. Cut it, and each piece will be found to have the two poles. Chop the string into dozens of pieces, and each fragment will test out as having two poles. Break a twig from a tree, and you will find the same thing. This page you are reading is the same, also.

Animals and insects also have powerful magnetism. Some time ago in Lima, Peru, there was a colony of termites which discharged electric currents of such intensity that the short-wave reception in their vicinity was disturbed.

Your body is a powerful magnet, your two hands being its major poles. Subtle Magnetism is flowing within them constantly. Your touching of this page is charging it with that Magnetism. Anything you touch becomes to some degree magnetized. A very sensitive person can detect this Magnetism, and we call that psychometry. There is nothing mysterious or supernatural about it at all. If you can project a very intense and grosser type of this Magnetism from your hands it is psychokinetic force. This is how psychics bend spoons, stop watches, etc.; and how Nelya Mikhailova, the Soviet psycho-kineticist made known through *Psychic Discoveries Behind the Iron Curtain*, could move objects–especially metal ones, which are the most sensitive to Magnetism–by moving her hands over them.

Your body is a magnet, as I have said, but that is oversimplifying things. It is really several magnets hooked together to act as one. The human body can be pictured as four magnets: three horseshoe magnets and one bar magnet. Your two feet are the poles of one horseshoe, your hands are the poles of another, and the right and left sides of your head are the third. The spine is connecting these three, running through the middle of the body as a bar magnet—its two ends being the two poles.

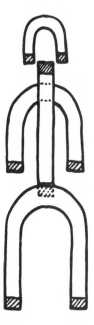

In this century a multitude of bioenergetic or vibrational healing machines of all types, some accepted by the medical profession and some not, have been invented and patented. But the perfect therapeutic apparatus, the truest healing machine, is your own body. "Therefore, of all the bodies, the one which can act most effectively upon man is his fellow-man," concluded Mesmer. Through your two hands that machine can be operated to restore health to yourself and others. Why? Because health is a harmonious, unobstructed flow of the life-force, and your hands can stimulate that life-force to flow through the body in a free and balanced way so the body can heal itself. Each person's body is the healer. You will never heal. Rather, the natural life-force whose flow you will increase or balance will do the healing. There is no other healer in the natural order of things. Even divine, supernatural healing is a restoration and regularization of that force. The same is true of medicine. Medicine only facilitates the body's self-repairing capacity. No matter what a medical doctor, osteopath, chiropractor, naturopath or herbalist prescribes, they are all one in the final analysis: life-force regulators.

Dr. A.S. Raleigh's analysis is thus: "We speak of heart disease, for instance, but as a matter of fact, we do not mean that the heart is diseased. Were anything to get wrong with the heart organically, the patient would not last very long. What we mean by heart disease is a weakened or disturbed condition of the cardiac nerve center, which causes the heart to get out of gear in the sense that the proper quantity of nervous stimuli is not communicated to the heart. The result is, the heart is not able to perform its functions; thus we say it is diseased; that is, it is out of harmony, so with all the other diseases that are to be included under the functional head.

"We should conceive of an organ or muscle as being a machine, a motor, in fact, or rather, a machine run by a motor.

The nerve center controlling this organ or muscle is the motor that runs the machine. Now, the analogy is perfect between the nerve center and the motor in ordinary machines; if the motor receives a proper quantity of electricity it will run the machine in the proper manner.... If the current of nervous stimuli flowing over the sympathetic nervous system and reaching the nerve center governing those organs, be normal, if the equilibrium be maintained, perfect health in those functions will be the result; each nerve center will receive a sufficient quantity of Prana to enable it to compel the organ to perform its proper functions. But if the current be weak or too strong or spasmodic, a corresponding result will take place....

"Any method which will restore the equilibrium in the circulation of the nerve force will cure any functional disease in the world. You may benefit the condition by applying nervous stimuli direct to the nerve center controlling the organ. Magnetic Healing has, therefore, been found of very much value in the treatment of functional diseases, because they give the nerve force for which that nerve center is starving. Giving this nerve force, they establish the equilibrium, they strengthen the organ or rather the nerve center, so that it makes the organ perform its proper functions....

"There is no disease of a functional character to which flesh is heir, that cannot be cured by this method and cured with comparative ease. There is no functional disease that can be cured permanently in any other way. Even those medicines such as arsenic and actina that are given by physicians, are really given for the purpose of accomplishing this result, by causing a certain stimulus to be imparted to the nerve centers in an artificial manner which will thus draw to them the nervous force.

"Remember, therefore, that in our method of healing we are employing the same fundamental principle that all intelligent physicians employ. Our methods are, of course, a little more scientific, they are more fundamental than theirs, but it is not a new departure, it is not a new fad, it is simply the application of the old physiological method of removing the cause and allowing Nature to take care of itself."

Once an osteopath was asked, while giving a treatment, what he was trying to accomplish, to which he replied, "I am releasing the life forces."

Advantages of Bio-Magnetic Therapy

Bio-Magnetic Therapy is the most basic and direct way of effecting that life-force, which we call Magnetism. And it has great advantages:

1) It can increase the flow of life-force into the body for general good health. Sickness need not be the only motivation for Magnetic treatment.

To live, the body must not only have a free circulation of life-force, it must have an inflowing of it from the world around it. Normally, this life-power enters the body through the feet, hands, and head. But if the body weakens in its magnetism—just as a magnet can become weakened—the supply of life-force is cut down to a level below that voltage needed for correct operation, and the magnetically starved (or suffocating) body becomes ill. Bio-Magnetic Therapy immediately increases the influx of vital power in the body and remagnetizes it, thus revitalizing its natural magnetic power of drawing life-force into itself. This is why Mesmer could state with such confidence: "It will be established from the facts, according to the rules which I will set forth, that Animal Magnetism will cure, immediately, all diseases of the nerves, and, mediately, all other diseases."

2) Bio-Magnetic Therapy can right away stimulate the supply and flow of life-force to a troubled area that has become vitality-starved through some obstruction. And in the increase of flow the obstruction is ultimately removed, just as a clogged water pipe can be cleared by flushing it out with an increased flow of water.

3) Some diseases are a result of a leaking out of the vital force from the body. Bio-Magnetic Therapy restores the normal channels of flow in the life-force and, in effect, seals the leaks.

4) Everything is divided into positive and negative, and the life-force is no exception. It, too, can become negative, disturbed, inert–even, we might say, diseased. Negative life-force accumulating in the body, especially through a blockage of this life-force's flow, can cause ill-health in the same way continual breathing of stale or foul air can cause devitalization and even illness. If it becomes localized, an organ becomes impaired in in its operation or even damaged. What is poison? It is any substance which imparts an energy or operation to the body that destroys its natural harmony and is antithetical to its normal functioning. So also, subtle life-force can be poison

to the body and its organs. Bio-Magnetic Therapy can remove this toxic magnetism in a very direct way.

5) Even if the flow of life-force is unobstructed, there will be problems if it is not flowing in the right channels—that is, if the polarity is confused, and the Magnetism is not flowing from the negative to the positive poles of the body as it should. Conflict in the Magnetic flow develops blockages, leaks, and deficiencies—in other words: *disease*. Bio-Magnetic Therapy corrects polarity as the first step in its application, whereas this vital aspect of of health is ignored in nearly all other systems of medicine and therapy.

Does this mean that Bio-Magnetic Therapy is a cure-all? Not at all! Bio-Magnetic Therapy does not cure; it simply aids the body to cure itself by supplying it with curative force. Nor should other modes of treatment be abandoned. Your body needs all the help it can get in this radioactive, polluted world of ours. But I do believe that Bio-Magnetic Therapy is an invaluable aid to health. Why?

First, it operates right at the heart of the disease—the life-force.

Second, it requires no diagnosis or prescribing of medicine or physical therapy.

Third, the only knowledge you need is that found in the practical principles of application which are given in this book. And they are so simple that once you learn them well they are yours forever. Remember: this system is *therapy*, not *medicine*. Knowledge of disease and its medicinal treatment is irrelevant to the application of Bio-Magnetic Therapy. Medicinal treatment of disease is the domain of trained practitioners of whatever school of medicine, and should not be trespassed upon.

Fourth, no tools are needed. Just your hands.

Fifth, everybody can do it.

Can you get more fundamental and universal than that? Bio-Magnetic Therapy stands on the broadest base of all: *Life*.

"Experience alone will scatter the clouds and shed light on this important truth: that NATURE AFFORDS A UNIVERSAL MEANS OF HEALING AND PRESERVING MEN"–Dr. Franz Anton Mesmer.

How is Bio-Magnetic Therapy applied? In the simplest way possible: by the application of the hands as poles of a magnet in order to increase and normalize the flow of life-force in your body and those of others.

Enough words! We can now get down to the how-to of it.

CHAPTER TWO:

HOW TO DO IT

The Number One Rule

At no time in Bio-Magnetic Therapy do we actually touch the body of those we are working with. Never. Rather, we hold our hands a short distance–two to four inches–from their body. After a while you will sense or feel just where to position your hands.

The etheric body of a person extends about one and a half inches from the physical body. To physically touch a person is to invade their etheric body and disrupt its natural functioning. Therefore Bio-Magnetic Therapy should always take place outside that inch and a half to be effective.

A Living Magnet

First, get acquainted with yourself as a living magnet. As I said before, your body is a great magnet composed of several magnets. But it is simple to formulate:

If You Are Right-Handed

1) Your right hand, your right foot, the right side of your head, and the entire right side of your body are *positive*.

2) Your left hand, your left foot, the left side of your head, and the entire left side of your body are *negative*.

If You Are Left-Handed

(1) Your left hand, your left foot, the left side of your head, and the entire left side of your body are *positive*.

2) Your right hand, your right foot, the right side of your head, and the entire right side of your body are *negative*.

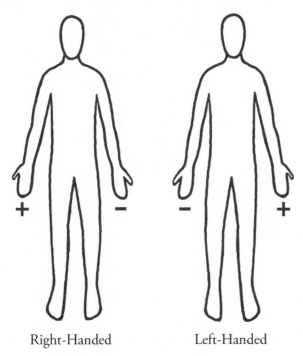

Right-Handed   Left-Handed

For Both Types of Handedness

In *both* right-handed and left-handed people, the spine is positive at the top and negative at the bottom (see next page).

Principles in Brief

Since you will be working with your hands only, all you really need to remember is:

(1) If you are right-handed, your right hand is *positive* and your left hand is *negative*.

(2) If you are left-handed, your left hand is *positive* and your right hand is *negative*.

(3) The same is true of anyone you are working on. So be sure and find out first thing whether they are right-handed or left-handed.

To Simplify

To avoid confusion and multiplication of words, I will just be using the terms "negative hand" and "positive hand" in the instructions. So it is important to memorize the above according to your handedness and that of those you work on. I will also be using the terms "operator" and "recipient" for the one doing the therapy and the one who is being worked upon.

Getting Ready

As you know, most magnets are metal, since that substance is the most easily magnetized. And we have all heard (or seen) that a steel needle when rubbed by a magnet becomes a magnet itself temporarily. The principle: metal attracts and absorbs Magnetism. Therefore metal can hinder the Magnetic flow where it contacts the body, either making it accumulate in just one spot rather than flow evenly, or it can draw it off from the body, causing a "leak." So the first step in applying Magnetism to yourself or others is to see that neither you nor the recipient are wearing any metal (jewelry, wristwatches, etc.), as this can interfere with the Magnetic flow. Metal in the body such as joint replacements, etc., may affect the therapy, but you should go right ahead as if it were not there.

During Bio-Magnetic Therapy, neither you nor the recipient should be touching metal. If the recipient will be sitting, be sure that the chair is not metal, or that the recipient is not touching any metal ornamentation on a non-metal chair. If the recipient is lying on a bed with a metal frame, be sure he is not touching it in any way or that you are not accidentally touching your leg against it while bending over him. A layer of cloth between will not insulate you or the recipient enough.

Also, neither you nor the recipient should be wearing wool or silk, as that insulates against Magnetism. Later, when you are proficient in detecting the subtleties of the Magnetic flow you may want to test whether certain man-made, synthetic fibers might not also hinder the Magnetic effect. Moreover, neither of you should be wearing leather belts or shoes, as this really blocks the Magnetic flow. Leather clothing is a hindrance also, and should be removed for Bio-Magnetic Therapy.

During the therapy the recipient should not have legs or arms crossed, his hands or feet touching one another, one of his hands touching the opposite arm or leg, or one of his feet touching the opposite leg.

If sitting for the therapy, the recipient should sit with feet flat on the floor, and his hands resting on his thighs (unless that interferes with you reaching a spot that needs treatment).

If lying down for the therapy, the recipient should lie flat on his back, or on his stomach, with his arms relaxed at his side–but his hands not touching his body–and his legs straight out and slightly separated so his feet do not touch each other.

Never should the recipient touch the operator or vice versa. Be sure that if you have to lean over the recipient you are not touching his body in any way. Otherwise a circuit will be formed that will interfere with the Magnetic flow.

The Four Methods

Basically there are four things to learn for the practice of Bio-Magnetic Therapy:

1) Polarity Correction
2) The Short Circuit
3) Drawing Out
4) Putting In

In these instructions the one giving the treatment is called the Operator, and the one being treated is called the Recipient.

CORRECTING POLARITY

All magnets have two poles and their interrelation is called polarity. Obviously the Magnetism in our bodies must be balanced and flowing correctly before we can either be treated or give treatment Magnetically. What exactly is polarity? Polarity is the way Magnetism is flowing in the body. Correct polarity is the steady, uninterrupted, flow of life-force from the negative poles of your body to the positive poles of your body. That is, the life-force is entering your body through your negative hand and foot, flowing through your entire system (just as blood flows through your veins), and then flowing out through your positive foot and hand. Perhaps an even more accurate example is your breathing. Your lungs take in fresh air; it is circulated through the body; and then you breathe out the air—now laden with the impurities and toxins collected by its passage through the body. Your body does the same thing with life-force. We can even say that your nervous system breathes, too. And just as illness and death can result from inadequate breathing or suffocation, so also inadequate or blocked flow of the life-force in your body can result in disease and even death.

Confused Polarity

Polarity can become confused as well as weakened or blocked. By "confused" we mean that the direction of its flow gets altered and switched around in parts of the body. This causes blockage, leaks, or malfunctioning of a body part–just as a motor will begin running backwards if you switch its poles. So a reversed, confused flow of life-force can make a body part "go haywire." So the first step in giving a treatment is to correct the recipient's polarity.

Checking Polarity

The best way to check for confused polarity is to have a person remove their shoes and put their feet up (or better, simply lie down). Then, Draw Out (this will be described later) from their positive foot. If the Magnetic flow is good and strong, then their polarity is fine, and they do not need any correction at that time. But if it is weak (maybe even coming in faint spurts) or undetectable, they need their polarity corrected.

Correcting Another's Polarity

I will give the description of Polarity Correction for another person, as it will make the instruction for correcting your own polarity easier to understand.

1) Have the recipient lie down, relaxed and with hands at the sides and legs slightly separated.

2) Hold your hands palm-downward, the fingers held straight out and parallel with the ground (the tips pointing in the direction of the recipient's head) three to five inches above the recipient's head.

A

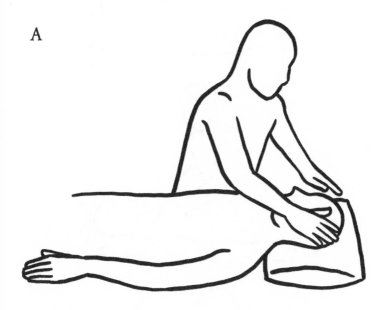

3) Beginning at the top of the recipient's head, cross and uncross your arms–palms downward toward the recipient–in a side-to-side sweeping motion, moving steadily down to the bottoms of the feet. Keep your hands three to five inches above the recipient's body.

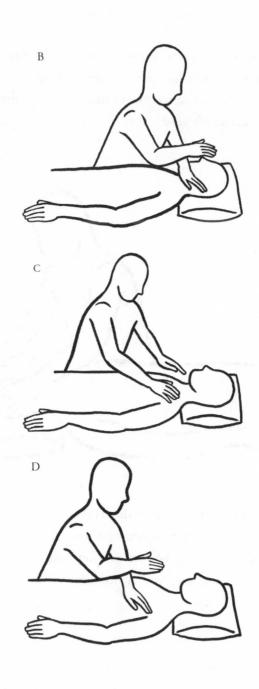

4) This is done the entire length of the recipient's body a total of four times:

a) Twice with your positive hand closer to the recipient, and your negative hand crossing above it.

b) Twice with your negative hand closer to the recipient, and your positive hand crossing above it.

(5) Do not move too rapidly toward the recipient's feet. Move down just a hand's breadth at the end of each sidewise sweep.

Correcting Your Own Polarity

1) Lie down.

2) Hold your two hands over your head, three to five inches above your body.

3) The fingers of your hands should be pointing toward the top of of your head. (See Fig. A.)

4) Using the same side-to-side sweep of the hands, as in correcting another's polarity, and moving down toward your feet after each sweep (see Figs. B, C and D), continue until you can no longer keep your hands positioned correctly and yet have your fingers pointing toward your head.

5) Turn your hands so the fingertips are toward your feet (see Fig. E); and continue on (see Fig. F) to just beyond your feet. Of course, you will have to sit up in order to move your hands over the lower parts of your body.

6) Do this four times as outlined in Correcting Another's Polarity.

Now your polarity is corrected.

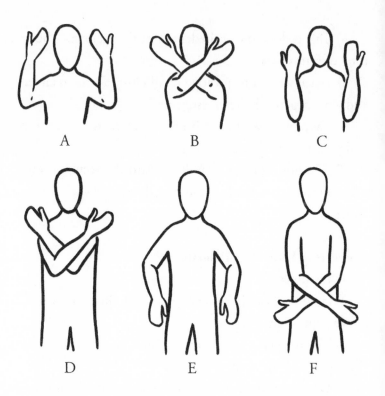

A   B   C

D   E   F

Do not underestimate the value of this simple Polarity Correction. Confused polarity causes many diseases and mental instability ("nerves"); and this Polarity Correction goes right to the root of the malfunction and corrects it.

Something really important about handedness

Some people who are left-handed were forced by families or schoolteachers to write and function as right-handed. This was/is damaging and can cause confusion and conflict in the person's nervous system and polarity. Definitely they should revert to their true handedness. So some people may need to recall if they were forced to "be" right-handed, but are really left-handed.

After years, how can you tell if you are right or left handed? There is no sure way I know of, but one thing you can do is correct someone's (or your) polarity three times in a row and then momentarily hold your negative hand by the sole of each foot in turn see which foot has magnetism flowing strongly out of it. That will be the positive foot and the hand on the same side will be the positive hand. Make sure of this.

How long should a Bio-Magnetic Therapy session be?

A session can be as long as it needs to be. However there is one rule: Do not work on a spot more than ten minutes during a session. Go back to it in the next session.

How often should a person receive Bio-Magnetic Therapy?

There should be a period of seventy-two hours (three days) between treatments to allow the treatment to thoroughly take hold and produce the maximum effect. Obviously, a few hours less than seventy-two between treatments will not harm, but it is good to stick to the full time between sessions. Also, the rules can be broken during emergencies and situations in which a person's life is in danger. But still be cautious and prudent.

THE SHORT CIRCUIT

The second technique is that which we call the Short Circuit. It consists simply of holding the two hands–palms facing each other (see below)–on opposite sides of the body or body part, such as the recipient's leg, arm, or head. The two hands should be positioned so that the fingers are also opposite one another and pointing in the same direction.

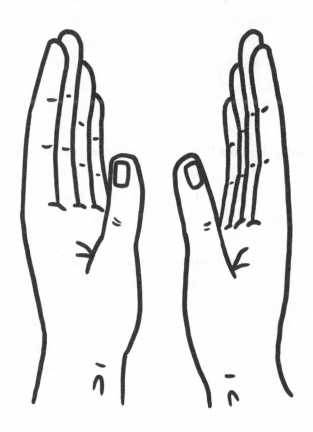

Although the Short Circuit can be used to good effect on the internal organs—especially lungs, heart, liver, kidneys, gall bladder, etc., it is very effective in the treatment of the joints of the body and also the vertebrae of the neck.

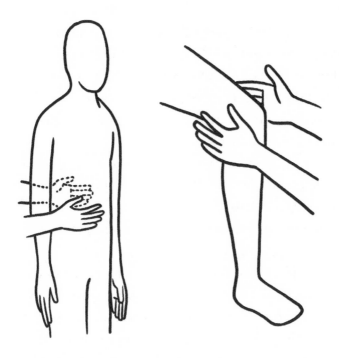

Holding the hands on opposite sides of the body part being treated–the palms turned toward each other–keep them there for at least three to five minutes or even longer. You do not actually touch the body, but hold your hands away from the body. I prefer about one-and-one-half inches from the body, but for most people the distance is three to six inches, and for some it is one foot away. You can pretty much just go by "feel" in this matter, placing your hands at whatever distance you feel is the most effective.

When working with the Short Circuit on a body organ or an area of the body, rather than on the head or joints, your negative hand should be behind and your positive hand in front, so the Magnetism will flow from your negative hand to your positive hand, thereby flowing into the part being treated. THE ONE EXCEPTION IS THE SHORT CIRCUIT ON THE HEART. In that situation, your negative hand should be in front of the heart area and your positive hand in back. This is most important.

You can apply the Short Circuit for as long as ten minutes in one position, but no longer (at one time, that is), unless the problem is gravely serious.

As a rule, you should never work on any spot for more than ten minutes at a time.

In applying the Short Circuit you may need to try a few positions in relation to the joints or vertebrae of the neck. For example, I have found that when using the Short Circuit on a joint it is consistently best to hold the hands on the sides of the joints or neck. But you may find instances where holding the hands in front and behind the joints or neck will be more effective.

Short Circuit on the head

The Short Circuit is usually employed on the head (hands on either side) to treat headaches or effect the pituitary gland (in cases of high or low blood pressure). It can also be used for treating the ears in some cases.

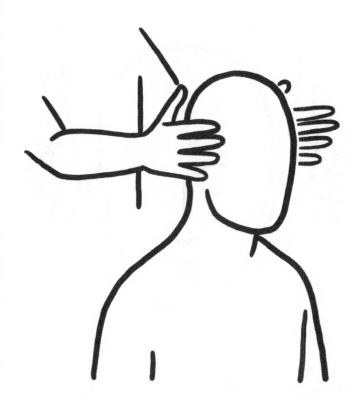

When working on the head, it is essential that we not confuse the recipient's polarity–which we will do if we are not careful. The head is itself a magnet: one side is positive and the other is negative–according to their handedness. Therefore the Magnetic flow in a person's head is naturally moving from negative to positive. (All Magnetism flows from negative to positive. It is a law of Magnetism.)

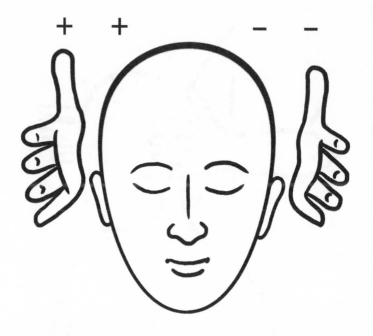

If the operator's negative hand is held on the negative side of the recipient's head, and the operator's positive hand is held on the positive side of the recipient's head, the Magnetic flow will be harmonious, for the Magnetism flowing from the operator's negative hand toward his positive hand will blend with that flowing from the negative side of the recipient's head to the positive side.

But if the operator's negative hand is held at the positive side of the recipient's head, and his positive hand on the negative side of the recipient's head, the flow between the operator's hands will conflict with the natural flow in the recipient's head, and the recipient's polarity will become confused or even reversed! I know this, because such a thing once happened to me when I was the recipient.

One operator placed his hands incorrectly in relation to the positive and negative sides of my head. Right away I felt much discomfort, but thought it was just a peculiar reaction on my part. After a while it became unbearable and I demanded that he stop the Short Circuit. Then we realized the cause of the problem. My polarity was corrected again by the operator and the Short Circuit done in the right way. This gave me relief from really terrible discomfort and headache, but a mild, ill-at-ease sensation persisted for a few hours.

So we must beware: *A misapplied Short Circuit is the only way in which we can harm a patient.* And it is no joke. It is my opinion (untested, unproved) that besides physical problems, much mental illness stems from confused polarity. As I say, this is no joke.

All right: how do we avoid misapplying the Short Circuit? The principle is this: ALWAYS hold your negative hand on the negative side of the recipient's head, and your positive hand on the positive side of the recipient's head. In brief: Match your polarity with that of the recipient.

Here is another short rule of thumb: If the recipient has the same handedness as you, stand behind him to do the Short Circuit (see A below). If the recipient has a different handedness than you, stand in front of him for the Short Circuit (see B below).

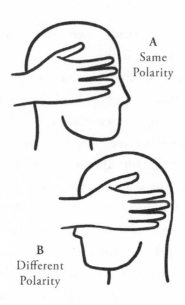

A
Same
Polarity

B
Different
Polarity

Now, just what is the nature of a Short Circuit? When you oppose the palms of your hands, you produce a Magnetic flow between them, from the negative hand to the positive hand,

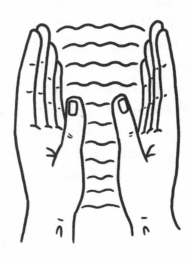

just as when two poles of a battery are connected or you oppose the positive pole of a magnet with the negative pole of another magnet. As I have said, your two hands are positive and negative poles of your body-magnet. So when you oppose your hands to each other on either side of a body part, the resulting Magnetic flow passes through that part, effecting it strongly. Not only does it correct the Magnetism of the body part, it can actually break up deposits in the joints and vertebrae. Later on we will be considering the use of the Short Circuit to actually crumble kidney and gall stones. The Short Circuit is even used sometimes in hospitals when a mild electric current is passed through the heart of cardiac patients, from back to front, by means of electrical equipment. So the principle of the Short Circuit is known to regular medicine as well.

Distance of the hands in Drawing Out and Putting In

Before taking up Drawing and Out and Putting in we should again consider the matter of how far the hands are held from the body of the recipient in those techniques—for we do not touch the body itself in Bio-Magnetic Therapy except in one instance which will be discussed later.

"Magnetism at a certain distance produces a greater effect than when it is applied immediately" (Mesmer). I find that holding my hands only about one-and-a-half inches from the recipient's body is most effective for me, and certainly makes it easier for me to feel the Magnetic flow. But usually people find that three to five inches is more comfortable or natural feeling to them. Some even find that they work best if they actually do place their hands on the recipient. But I urge you to try applying Magnetism without actually touching the recipient before you decide definitely that you need to place your hands directly on those you treat. This is because the sensitivity of your hands to the Magnetic flow will be hindered by the sensations of clothing texture. Even more important, since you need to be guided by the sensations of heat or electrical flow emanating from the leaks of the recipient's body, you may mistake the recipient's natural body heat for the heat of Magnetic leaks. Also, the recipient sometimes should guide you by his sensations of the Magnetism flowing to him from your hands, and if your hands are touching him the warmth he will feel from your hands may interfere with that.

If, however, you find you cannot effectively apply Magnetism except by laying your hands directly on the recipient's body, then go right ahead. But do keep in mind that you will not always be able to rely on either your own or the recipient's sensations of heat-flow. Further, as previously said, the sensation of touching the recipient's clothes may cancel out your feeling of the Magnetic flow from your hands. Although this is not absolutely essential, it is a major factor in helping the operator know when he has worked long enough on a particular spot.

DRAWING OUT

Next we come to the most commonly used technique of Bio-Magnetic Therapy: Drawing Out.

Hippocrates wrote: "It has often appeared while I have been soothing my patient that there was a strange property in my hands to pull and draw away from the affected parts aches, and diverse impurities, by laying my hand upon the place." He was referring to Drawing Out.

This method has a fourfold benefit: (1) It increases the flow of life-force into the body; (2) it removes blockages of the life-force; (3) it causes diseased or damaged parts of the body to become saturated with life-force and thus stimulates the healing power of the body; (4) it removes negative life-force that may have accumulated in a particular area of the body. This fourth point is perhaps the most important, especially in dealing with disease caused by poisons in the organs or tissues. It is also of prime importance in treating cysts and tumors. Except for the few types of problems where the Short Circuit or Putting In is of more benefit, the method of Drawing Out is to be used in treating most complaints. This one method can be used in all situations, but there are times when the others will produce a quicker result. The method of Drawing Out is this:

1) Place your negative hand–open with the palm toward the recipient's body–over the area of the body where there is pain or disease: not touching the body, but above it at the distance you have found best for you.

2) Hold your positive hand out and down, open with the palm turned downward and parallel to the ground as in the illustration below.

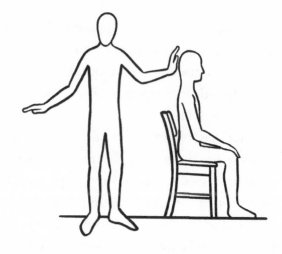

You may feel heat, stinging, or tingling in the palm of both hands. By holding your hands in this way you make your body into a great, drawing magnet. The life-force begins flowing from the recipient's trouble spot, through your negative hand and arm, and out through your positive arm and hand. Thus Drawing Out accomplishes all the four effects listed at the beginning of this section. And right away.

At this point three questions arise:

If you draw life-force out of the recipient's body, won't the recipient's body become depleted of life-force?

Answer: No. Just the opposite. The human body is set up to be continually drawing life-force into itself and throwing it off. This is done by means of the poles of the body-magnet. When the life-force becomes blocked the body's drawing power is weakened. But if you begin drawing from any spot of the body, the impeded clogged life-force is freed, begins to flow vigorously, and automatically the influx of life-force is increased. Thus, even though you may be working on only one spot, the entire body becomes revitalized. Many times, as you are Drawing Out, sensitive recipients will feel tingling or warmth in their negative hands and feet as the flow of life-force into their bodies is stimulated.

If you draw negative life-force from ill recipients through your own body, will you then become ill?

Answer: There is a definite possibility that if negative life-force becomes lodged in your body, you may become ill yourself. This can be avoided by three things:

a) When you are finished Drawing Out, slowly move your negative hand away from the recipient's body, and raise it in the position shown below.

Hold this position for about thirty seconds. By doing this you will draw pure life-force into yourself and any negative life-force between the two poles of your hands will flow right on out of your positive hand–which should still be held down and out, away from the recipient.

b) To further insure getting rid of all negative life-force, you must unfailingly wash your hands carefully as will be described after the instructions for Putting In.

c) You must keep your own body in good health. Good health creates a positive Magnetism in the body that can counteract and neutralize negative Magnetism. But health must be maintained! This is why I have included a section on Staying Healthy.

How long should a person Draw Out from a recipient?

Answer: The average time is five to ten minutes on one spot (though you may treat many spots in a treatment). The maximum time for treatment of a single spot is ten minutes. (Why will be discussed later.) Of course, you can work on many spots–the limit is just on the time on any particular spot.

Small "Hot Spots"

Often, when Drawing Out you will feel heat or "electricity" emanating from the recipient's body to your palm. Then, after a while–sometimes quickly or sometimes only after several minutes–the sensation of heat or electrical tingling in your palm ceases. When this occurs the leak is sealed, the negative Magnetism has been removed from that area. Then you should stop Drawing Out from that particular spot. In subsequent treatments, though, test the spot again, and if you feel heat, then Draw Out again.

What if a recipient has pain in a spot and you feel no heat or electrical tingling there?

Answer: Chances are the pain is symptomatic of a problem in another area. But go ahead and Draw Out from the place of pain for five to ten minutes (stopping if the pain stops during that time). Since that spot is paining, it is somehow connected with the actual trouble spot, and Drawing Out from it will effect the real problem area. Once, for two days I had a terrible sinus headache–or so I thought. The morning of the second day I had had enough of it, so I asked one of our monastery residents to do Magnetic for me, and Draw Out from my aching sinuses. (I was so long in getting treated because I had not much experience with Magnetism then, and still could hardly believe its effectiveness.) He began Drawing Out, and immediately I had the peculiar sensation of a magnetic "cord" running down to my stomach and drawing it upward. It felt just as though a magnet were pulling on it. So I told him to quit Drawing Out from my head and instead Draw Out from my stomach area. He did so for only a few minutes, and that was the end of the headache! But if I had not been sensitive like that, working on my head area would still have helped, for it was the effecting of the stomach that I was feeling in that pulling sensation.

Are there situations when Drawing Out should not be done?

Answer: Yes! NEVER Draw Out from the heart or the solar plexus.

Only Put In (to be discussed next) to the heart or the solar plexus. When there is a problem with the heart, and you feel that Drawing Out is called for, then Draw Out from the back—just opposite the heart.

Using Your Hands As Sensors

Drawing Out has another function besides simple treatment. Through the Drawing Out positioning of your hands, you can use your negative hand as a sensor to search out trouble spots and, after treating them, to tell when the Magnetism is corrected.

All diseases or physical malfunctions emanate a Magnetic field or flow that is picked up by the palm as heat or electrical tingling in Drawing Out. When that Magnetism enters your negative palm as it is being drawn out, the palm feels this as heat, tingling, stinging, etc. Often the same sensation is felt by the palm of your positive hand as it leaves your body. Whenever such sensations are picked up by your palm, stay on that spot and Draw Out, remembering the ten-minute rule. When the sensation stops (not just lessens), move the palm over the nearby area where you may encounter milder or more intense "hot spots." If so, Draw Out from these, too. Sometimes you may feel heat in your fingertips, but not the palm: *only pay attention to the palm.* I am saying "palm," but frequently people feel heat not in the middle of the palm (I do) but at the base of the palm, the "heel" of the hand. That is also correct and reliable.

Anyhow, use your negative palm and its sensations to determine how long to Draw Out. Sometimes you will pass over a hot spot, pause, and the sensation will fade away in a matter of seconds. Why? Because it is simply an emanation from a nerve plexus connected with a troubled area. Several times I have checked the positions of these hot flashes on an Acupuncture chart and found that they corresponded to Acupuncture points.

But what if the heat, tingling, or stinging does not stop after ten minutes of Drawing Out? You should stop Drawing Out on that particular spot anyway, and come back to it in the next treatment. This is of prime importance, as will be explained later in the section on Reactions.

One thing you may encounter: while Drawing Out, the sensation of heat suddenly turns to *cold*. This means the polarity has changed, the leak has sealed, and you need no longer continue working on that spot. This is very rare, but you may come across it in your work with Magnetism.

Two Hints On Increasing The Efficiency of Drawing Out

1) Since you are making your body into a magnet it will definitely assume a relationship with the greater magnet of the earth. We have found that the effectiveness of Drawing Out is markedly increased if the fingers of your positive hand (which is being held down and parallel with the floor, the palm facing downward) are pointing toward the South.

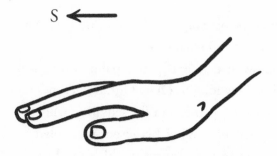

This was discovered by Mesmer, who wrote: "If the current of the Magnetism concurs in its direction with the general current, or with the Magnetic current of the earth, the general result is an increase of intensity of all these currents."

2) As I will be discussing later, you do not visualize or affirm that the Magnetism is flowing through you. Rather, you should be calm, even detached, and let the natural flow of the Magnetism take place. But it has been found that if you make yourself very aware of (intently "feel") the sensations of your two palms, especially the positive one, the Magnetic flow will increase. Be sure that you are just being aware of the palms, not directing the Magnetic flow in any way.

I hope you will read over this section on Drawing Out several times because there are so many important points in it that are essential to correct, effective practice.

PUTTING IN

Drawing Out is the usual technique of Bio-Magnetic Therapy. However, you may find some instances where Drawing Out makes the recipient (or even you) very uncomfortable, perhaps even greatly increasing pain in an area. At such a time you may find that Putting In will be more comfortable for the recipient or you. Also, if on some occasion your own vitality is somewhat lowered and you are not too sure that your body could handle any absorption of negative energy from a recipient, you might want to use Putting In. It is, however, my experience that Putting In is not as effective as Drawing Out, as a rule. Once, though, I found that one recipient's cracked rib responded best to Putting In.

The method of Putting In is this:

1) Place your positive hand over the part of the recipient's body to be treated.

2) Raise your negative hand over your head, with the palm facing directly upward and your fingers spread and curved as though you are holding a ball in your hand.

3) Just keep that position as long as you wish to be working on the recipient.

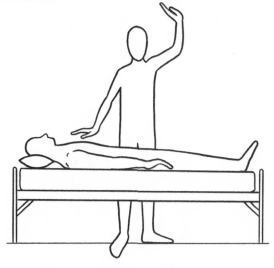

In a book on Egyptian antiquities by Montfaucon, a painting is described in which healers are treating a sick person by holding their hands in the Putting In positions. Until the discovery of Bio-Magnetic Therapy, such pictures were a great mystery to scholars.

When the recipient has very low vitality it is always good to Put In at some time in a session. Usually you will Put In at the solar plexus, but it can be done at any point you feel needs it.

WASHING YOUR HANDS

After any session of bio-magnetic therapy wash your hands immediately–no delay!!!

Otherwise some negative energies may remain in your body from the recipient and you may get their illness. This is very serious. I do not want you to be afraid to practice Bio-Magnetic Therapy, but I do want you to be aware that this has very inflexible rules that must be observed if you and those you treat are to really benefit from it.

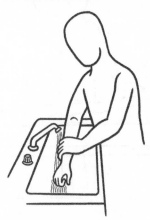

Wash your hands and forearms in *cold* water. Running water is best, but if you do not have it at hand, then use a basin of cold water and swish your hands and forearms around in the water vigorously. Then "squeegie" the water off each hand and forearm with the opposite hand. And then "squeegie" off each finger individually. If you are using a sink that has a metal spigot it is also good to touch the spigot with all your fingertips and thumbs. This will also help in drawing off any negative Magnetism you have collected on your hands. This is always done after any Magnetic work (including Long Distance), no matter how slight, for it is possible to pick up the recipient's disorders if the negative Magnetism is not eliminated from your hands and body.

For the same reason you NEVER allow anyone to be in the room where you are working on someone.

A Hint To Increase Effectiveness

As in Drawing Out, it helps to orient yourself with the Magnetism of the earth. I have found that if your negative hand is held with the heel of your hand toward the North–as though your curved fingers were poised to catch a ball thrown from the North–it increases the Magnetic flow considerably.

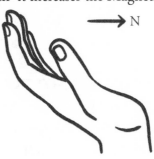

As in Drawing Out, if when doing Putting In your positive hand feels a sensation of cold, it means that the leak in the recipient's body is sealed, and you need no longer work on that particular spot in that treatment. (This does not mean you should not work on it in future treatments.) Sometimes you may feel your palms being repelled–pushed away from the recipient–as though a balloon is being squashed between your hand and the recipient's body. That, too, indicates that the leak is sealed, and no more Magnetism is entering the recipient's body at that particular spot.

Clearing The Room

After every treatment with Bio-Magnetic Therapy, the room should be cleared of any negative Magnetism that may have been drawn out into the air. You do not want to have negative Magnetism circulating around to be absorbed by you or others who enter the room. To do this, open the windows and have a fan blowing out. It is also very good to burn incense in the room. Sandalwood incense is the absolute best, but frankincense mixed with a little Benzoin (Sumatra) is excellent. Almost always I have stick incense burning during a session, and if the weather permits I have the windows and doors open. (It is excellent to do Bio-Magnetic Therapy out of doors in good weather.)

WHAT YOU DO NOT DO

You do not heal. You enable the body to heal itself.

You do not diagnose. This is the province of qualified medical practitioners. Anyway, we are simply working on the

Magnetism of the body, not on disease or even the body itself, so we have no need to diagnose. We are not practicing medicine, we are simply balancing the Magnetism of the body and facilitating its natural curative property.

You do not mentally will or direct the Magnetic energy. The simple placement of your hands is sufficient. In this way you ensure that the Magnetic flow is natural, and therefore the most effective.

You do not suggest, affirm or visualize in any way. If you do, you limit and hinder the flow of Magnetism, which is a force much greater and more subtle than mere mental energy. To attempt mental manipulation of this fundamental force is to actually decrease its effectiveness. The temptation to play healer must be resisted, both for your own sake and that of the recipient. The great Magnetic therapist, F. W. Sears, wrote: "Every life is a vital center through which the All-Health energy of the universe is pouring all the time, when it is not obstructed by our own personal thought currents. I never use my personal energy. There is where many healers make a big mistake. They have a consciousness that it is their personal force, their personal self, their personal power that is healing the patient. The result is they give of themselves, and while it is true they effect some cures, such cures are at the expense of their own vitality. This occurs only when we use a personal force, for the law of the personal plane of consciousness is destructive. So in giving treatments we should never live in the consciousness that it is our personal force, that it is we who are doing it. Live in the consciousness that we are the connecting link through which the All-Health energy of the universe is pouring, just as the pipe which conducts the water from the source of supply is the connecting link between the source and the faucet."

AN EXTRA PRACTICE: THE BODY SWEEP

When I speak of Bio-Magnetic Therapy I am speaking of the system developed by Ina Bryant, though there are various other practices that could be considered Bio-Magnetic Therapy since they deal with bio-energy. I want to include a very valuable practice that is not part of Ina's system: the Body Sweep. I learned this from a man who had been taught it by a Yaqui Indian medicine man. So here it is for you to try.

Magnetism is not only flowing through and throughout the body, it is also circulating around it in a measurable magnetic field. This is the "aura" we so often hear about. This magnetic field also becomes disturbed or weakened, and sometimes negative life-force circulates in the aura before being absorbed by the body and causing disease or lowered vitality. The Body Sweep therefore does two things: it stimulates the healthy flow of Magnetism around the body, balances and regulates that flow, and eliminates negative life-force that might be there. Further, it draws a considerable portion of any negative life-force out of the body, and eliminates it. This is a fundamental healing method, and is of inestimable worth. Here is how it is done:

1) Have the recipient either sit on a chair or stand (I prefer the recipient standing). Be sure they are standing or sitting with enough room for you to walk around them in a circle.

2) Stand directly in front of the recipient.

3) Cup your hands slightly, and bring them up and hold them, palms down and thumbs touching, about one inch over the recipient's head. Even closer is all right, but the recipient's body should not be touched in the Body Sweep.

4) Slowly and smoothly—with hands still cupped and palms held downward—separate your hands and move them down on either side of the recipient's head and neck; along the shoulders; down the sides of his arms (which should be hanging relaxed by his side) and on down the rest of his body and sides of his legs to the floor, keeping your hands near the body—no more than one inch away, less, if it is possible to do so without touching it.

Note that the hands are always on opposite sides of the recipient's body, as though his body was a pivot point around which your hands are turning on an axis.

5) Then, forming your hands into fists, rise up and at the same time flick your fingers outward while shaking your hands also outward with a "snap" away from the recipient's body, as though shaking off the negative energy gathered by your hands. *Remember: never turn the palms of your hands toward the recipient when doing this. Instead, always keep the hands slightly cupped and palms downward when making the sweeping motions.*

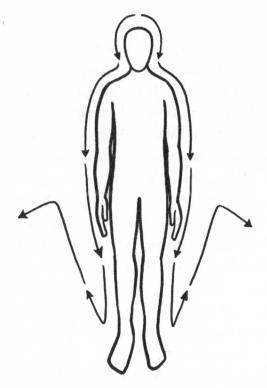

6) Bring your hands back up to above the recipient's head with an outward curving sweeping motion, again cupping them and being sure that the palms are turned downward. (As I said, imagine that your two hands are moving on an axis with the recipient's body as the pivot point.) Thus the hands are always directly opposite to one another with the recipient's body always in between them.

7) With this imaginary axis in mind, turn your hands slightly on a clockwise pivotal movement, and again bring them down over the recipient's body in the sweeping motion. This time, however, your right hand will not be at the exact

side of the head and body, but rather about a palm's breadth over to the right—more toward the front of the recipient's face. Coming down further, your right hand will be to the right of where it was before, and thus just in front of his left arm and the trunk of his body. Your left hand will be just behind his right shoulder. Again, after you have swept down the whole length of his body, shake your hands out as outlined above.

8) Return your hands to above the recipient's head—cupped slightly and palms held downward.

9) This time you move the hands on their imaginary axis a little further in a clockwise circle, and again make a full body sweep. This time your right hand will be descending nearly in front of the center of the recipient's face, and your left hand will be nearly opposite his spine. After completing the sweep to the floor, shake your hands, flicking the fingers, as described, and again return the hands to above bis head.

10) This time when you sweep down, your right hand will be descending right in the center of the recipient's face, just in front of his nose, and your left hand will be passing directly down the line of the spine. (Remember not to touch him.)

11) In this way, keep moving your hands on the imaginary axis and sweeping down to the floor, until you have circled him completely, and find yourself standing in front of the recipient in your original position.

12) Repeat the above, entire process at least once—if not twice—more. This completes the Body Sweep.

For seriously ill persons, you may wish to do the Body Sweep several times in succession.

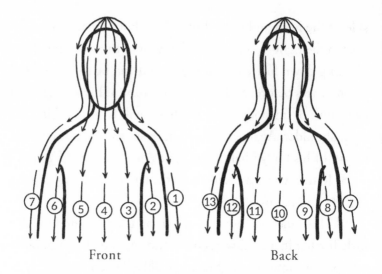

Front   Back

I find that when working with an average-size adult it takes twelve sweeps in this way to circle around the recipient thoroughly (see above). And thoroughness counts greatly here. Think of the body as divided into four parts: (1) Left shoulder to center of face; (2) Center of face to right shoulder; (3) Right shoulder to center of back (spine); (4) Center of back to left shoulder. And three sweeps are required to cover each area. Naturally, there will be some overlapping on the head and neck since their circumference is so small. But that is all right.

Four Important Points

Four things are crucial in doing the Body Sweep:

(1) Keep your hands cupped throughout the downward sweep.

(2) Keep your hands held with palms down throughout the sweep and NEVER turn them toward the recipient.

(3) Form your hands into fists after each sweep and then flick out the fingers away from the recipient, while snapping your hands in a shaking motion (also away from the recipient) when rising up to begin the next sweep.

(4) Wash your hands immediately after doing this.

CHAPTER THREE:

THERAPY ROUTINES

First, be sure that you are yourself in good health! Never, never work on anyone else when you are not in good shape. Otherwise you might pass on some of your illness (no matter how minor) to them, and in your weakened resistance will absorb their problems. In this way you will just be playing a game of musical chairs with illness. Do not do it–for your sake and that of the recipient.

Although in a pinch we can work on just trouble spots, it is always best to give a full treatment, which is as follows.

Basic Routine

1) First see that neither you nor the recipient are wearing any metal or material (silk, wool, or leather) which can impede the Magnetic flow. Also, that neither you nor the recipient are touching metal in any way.

2) Check the recipient's polarity as described in the last chapter. If it needs correction, do so. (Your own polarity should have already been corrected.)

3) Work on known trouble spots with the Short Circuit, Drawing Out or Putting In, not working on a spot longer than ten minutes.

4) Make a thorough search of the recipient's body, holding your hands in the Drawing Out position and carefully moving your negative hand—at a slight distance—over the recipient's entire body, both front and back, using your negative hand as a sensor to pick up the sensations of heat or electrical flow which indicate leaks or problems in the body. Wherever you find heat or electrical tingling, Draw Out from that spot (or Put In or apply the Short Circuit, if that seems best) until the sensations stop or ten minutes have passed. Then move on.

5) When done stand up and assume the Putting in Stance for a while to let any negative energy flow out of you.

6) WASH YOUR HANDS. Always.

How many treatments should a person have?

A person with a specific problem should be treated until the problem is removed; and then at least three more treatments should be given to make sure the problem is truly removed and not just alleviated or in abeyance.

"Do not be deceived with the idea that the relief which follows a Magnetic treatment is permanent—that is to say, that a chemical change has taken place and that the symptom is permanently cured because it has disappeared. The relief which follows a Magnetic treatment is due to the fact that artificial stimulus has been supplied to the nerve centers. They are able to do their work much more effectively than they did before, but they are doing this work with a force other than their own. After a while, in the course of time, it will be discovered that the special stimulus has been exhausted, consequently the patient will be in the same condition as before. The Magnetic treatments, therefore, must be continued for some time after the patient is apparently cured, until the defect has been removed, and the patient has had a chance to accumulate the necessary amount of energy unto the successful performance of the work.

"In a word, a permanent cure is one thing; the relief of disease symptoms by Magnetic treatment is quite another" (Dr. A.S. Raleigh).

Can you overload the recipient with Magnetism?

No, because when the amount of Magnetism in the recipient is brought up to the right level, no more will be absorbed by him. As mentioned before, you may even feel a cold sensation in your palm, or have the sensation that your hand is being repelled from the surface of his body, much like the feeling of having a balloon squashing between his body and your hand.

This is one of the advantages of Bio-Magnetic Therapy. A person can take too much of a certain kind of medicine– or even the wrong kind of medicine. But in Bio-Magnetic Therapy this cannot happen. Actually, one of the criteria of health is that exteriorly applied Magnetism ceases to effect the recipient. When this happens, they are well. Magnetism is a universal force that operates by precise laws of need and supply. Not one unit is wasted. The moment a recipient needs no more Magnetism, in that moment Magnetism ceases to flow to him from the operator. This does not mean that no further therapy is needed, but *at that moment* the maximum has been accomplished.

Even a person without any specific problem would do well to have a full Magnetic treatment periodically.

How often should a person be treated?

You should not treat a recipient within less than seventy-two hours after the previous treatment, unless some new problem arises that requires attention. This is because Bio-Magnetic Therapy, simple though it may be, affects the body profoundly. Therefore enough time must be given for the recipient's body to adjust before further treatment. For this reason, no one should have their eyes tested or have a physical examination (unless ill) within seventy-two hours after a Magnetic treatment, because the reactions and adjustments the body undergoes might cause an incorrect result in the test. It is actually a very good thing for the recipient to fall asleep and sleep for some time after the therapy as the body is adjusting itself to the effects of the treatment.

Reactions

Considering the foregoing, this is the appropriate point to discuss *reactions*. Bio-Magnetic Therapy is not a surface treatment: it deals with the fundamental element of our physical existence: life-force, itself. So when we undergo Magnetic treatment a profound change occurs. The effect is *natural*, but a Magnetic treatment can so revitalize the body that many toxins are expelled by the newly-energized system. As a result a recipient may temporarily even feel worse than he did before the treatment. This is not the rule, but it does happen. For this reason we do not work on a spot more than ten minutes at one time nor before seventy-two hours have elapsed between treatments. Consequently reactions should rarely result, if ever. But if they do, we understand their nature and do not worry. Magnetism is a life-saver and a life-preserver, but you can injure yourself by overdosing on anything–even oxygen. By adhering to the rules regarding length and frequency of treatment, only benefit will result from your practice.

Exceptions?

Are there any exceptions to the ten-minutes-seventy-two-hours-apart rule? Almost none. As I said before, if the case is very serious, and a reaction would not be as bad as the present state of the problem, you might cautiously work a little more or a little more frequently. Some types of problems actually require a longer working time, such as kidney stones (to be discussed later in this chapter). But here, especially, discretion is indeed the better part of valor.

Increased Sensitivity To Medicine

Another type of reaction is increased responsiveness to medication. Therefore the recipient who is taking medication of any kind, including herbal or natural remedies, should watch carefully to see if he needs to reduce the amount of medication. This should be carefully explained to those who take medications such as insulin.

On the positive side, we can see that since Magnetism so assists the action of medicine, those who are going to "regular doctors" can benefit from this therapy.

KIDNEY STONES AND GALLSTONES

Although I have said that we work on the Magnetism of the body, and not on diseases or specific problems, we naturally are going to encounter situations where a qualified doctor has diagnosed the problem for the recipient. One of the most amazing benefits Bio-Magnetic Therapy can impart is in the alleviation of Kidney Stones and Gallstones. Just as Magnetism can break up and disperse deposits in joints (through the Short Circuit), so also it can dissolve these stones. The process is not simple, and can take some hours. Here it is:

Kidney Stones

1) Place your hands so as to be doing a Short Circuit on the affected kidney. In this method, you actually place your hands on the recipient's body. As we usually place the positive hand in front and the negative hand in back when working on other organs, so also in the case of stones we place our positive hand in front and the negative hand in back.

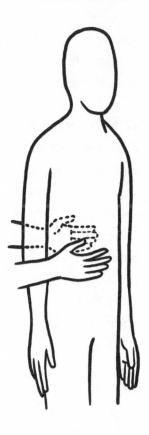

In this way the Magnetic current passes through the kidney toward the front of the body. Keep your hands in the Short Circuit position until the recipient feels that the stones have passed out of the kidney into the ureter, under your positive hand. He may have a sensation of the pain moving forward to your positive hand, or he may have the feeling of "worms crawling" in the direction of your hand.

2) When the recipient feels that the stone(s) has passed into the ureter, then place your negative hand over the spot

where your positive hand had been, and place your positive hand over the recipient's bladder.

3) When the discomfort or "crawling" which the recipient will feel between your two hands has stopped, move your negative hand to the spot over the bladder where your positive hand had been. Then place the index finger and middle finger of your positive hand on the recipient's pubic bone–the fingertips pointing toward the recipient's head (see the following illustration).

If you apply light pressure, you should be able to feel two small indentations for the tips of the fingers to fit into.

4) When the recipient feels the urge to urinate, take your hands away slowly, so he can use the toilet. You might want the recipient to urinate into a special container so you can see if particles of the stone have actually been passed. (Frequently the stones are so thoroughly dissolved by the Magnetism that no particles large enough to be seen remain.)

Notice that in this method you stay on the spot much longer than the normal ten minutes—in fact, you stay as long as an hour or more, if need be.

Obviously, the above method should not be used on a person undergoing a kidney stone attack. Then it is too late, and the sufferer should be taken to a hospital or doctor's office immediately. If, of course, you were miles from any medical facility, it would be good to apply the Short Circuit while on the way to the doctor or hospital, as this could greatly alleviate the pain.

Gallstones

For Gallstones, the process is similar, though not so complex.

1) Do a Short Circuit on the gall bladder as outlined in the routine for Kidney Stones.

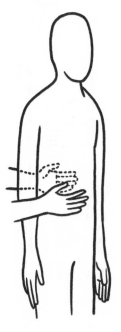

Be sure your negative hand is behind the recipient's body and your positive hand in front. Here, too, you actually touch the recipient's body.

2) Hold the Short Circuit until the recipient feels through discomfort or a "crawling" sensation that the stones have passed out–or are passing out–into the bile duct.

3) Then, with your negative hand still held as before, behind the back of the recipient, begin stroking with your positive hand downward toward the duodenum.

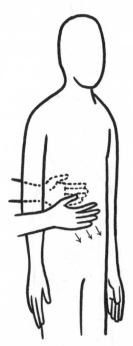

4) After the stones have gone into the duodenum, you need bother no more, as they will from there on be eliminated through the intestines.

The same remarks made in reference to the crumbling and passing of kidney stones given above applies to this method.

Sciatica

1) Do a Short Circuit, not touching the body, by placing your hands at the sides of the recipient (BE SURE your negative hand is on the recipient's negative side and your positive hand on the positive side), about two inches toward the back, where the muscles form an indentation above the hip joint.

2) Draw Out over the Sciatic Nerve at the hip joint. Five minutes on each side.

3) Draw Out from the base of the spine.

Constipation

Do a Short Circuit on the bowels (negative hand in back). Move around to various places, and the recipient should actually feel a "breaking up" sensation. Basically, do as is outlined in the section on Kidney and Gall Stones, even to placing the negative hand above and the positive hand at the base of the spine (not touching the body), near the anus. Be sure a toilet is near at hand!

Headaches

Most headaches can be relieved with the Short Circuit. You may need to move around a little bit to find the hot spots. If the Short Circuit does not give complete relief, then search the head and Draw Out.

Migraine headaches can be greatly relieved–and in some cases completely eliminated–in this way, especially if Magnetic is applied from the very beginning of the attack, and again two or three more times that day.

Sinus headaches can really be helped with Drawing Out over the sinus cavities.

Joint Problems

Pain, stiffness, and swelling in the joints can be worked on with the Short Circuit. Side to side seems best, but there is no reason why you should not experiment with front-to-back.

Teeth

Magnetism is no substitute for a good dentist, but I have found that tooth pain and especially infection can be helped by Drawing Out. Naturally, cavities and structural problems cannot be cleared up with Magnetism.

Broken Bones

To speed the healing of broken bones after they are set, apply the Short Circuit especially, but Drawing Out should be tried as well. Even Putting In. See how the recipient feels.

Spine and Coccyx Problems

For bone-related problems, it has been found that Drawing Out greatly helps in actual readjustment of bones (vertebrae). When the problem is muscle spasm (usually bone and muscle problems go together), Putting In seems to work the best to relax the muscles.

Use Magnetism to get some relief for these problems, but search out a really good Chiropractor (something I have only managed four times in over half a century) or good *adjustment-oriented* Osteopath for treatment.

Low Vitality

In cases of low vitality and general debility the Body Sweep and Putting In at the solar plexus (pit of stomach) will be found to help a great deal.

A Further Suggestion

For some recipients it has been found to be more effective if the operator usually Puts In on any spot on the negative side of their body and Draws Out from places on the positive side of their body. Experiment alone will tell when this is the case.

Something to Try

In my experiments with Magnetism I have observed that the Magnetic flow is markedly enhanced if a recipient who is being treated lying down turns his hands up at right angles to his body so both his palms and the soles of his feet are "facing" in the same way.

This is not essential but it does help. I have tried having the operator close his eyes and simply pick up the "feel" of the Magnetic flow, and in one hundred percent of the tests the operator would always be able to tell when the recipient had "lifted his flippers." Try it for yourself.

You Can Treat Yourself

You can apply some of the methods outlined in this book such as the Short Circuit, Drawing Out and Putting In to help yourself. I believe that it is better to have someone else work on you, but when that is not possible, then apply what you have learned.

Team Treatment

There may be a time when you will want to work on a person with greatly increased magnetic force, especially if the recipient really needs rapid assistance. (But do not forget about possible reactions.) To boost your own Magnetism you can have another person help you in working. Here are the ways:

1) In the techniques of Drawing Out and Putting In, you will find your work greatly facilitated if you have a second operator holding on to the feet (shoes removed, of course) of the recipient. Be sure that the second operator does not confuse the recipient's polarity. The rule is: The second operator holds the *negative* foot of the recipient with his *positive* hand; and the *positive* foot of the recipient with his *negative* hand. This increases the Magnetic flow in the recipient, and itself

can clear up many problems. The effect will be as when two magnets become locked together.

Although I speak of the second operator holding the recipient's feet, it is not necessary for him to actually hold them (though I prefer it, myself). The second operator can hold his hands two or three inches away from the bottoms of the recipient's feet, and it will work just fine. Whatever you are most comfortable with.

Here I should mention a rule in Bio-Magnetic Therapy that I have not found a place to put in elsewhere: *Never should the recipient's arms or legs be crossed during a treatment; nor should the operator ever cross his arms or legs during a treatment.*

So the immediate question is: If the above is so, how then can a right-handed person hold on to the feet of a left-hander, or vice-versa? The answer is that he will have to stand or sit with his back to the recipient and reach his hands behind himself to do so. Awkward, indeed, but necessary. Of course, if the recipient is lying down, at some time–either when he is lying on his back or is lying on his stomach–this will have to be done, no matter what handedness the second operator and recipient may be. But for working frontwise, the simple rule is: *Face those of your same handedness; turn your back on those of different handedness.*

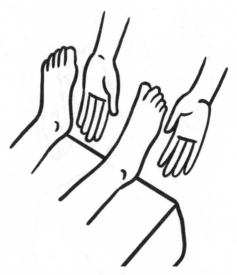

This rule applies when you and the recipient are facing each other, or when the recipient is lying on his back (when you are the second operator and needing to hold his feet). *If, however, the recipient is lying on his stomach, the rule is reversed:* if he has the same handedness as you, then you must turn your back and reach behind you. But if he has a different handedness, then you face him and easily grasp onto his feet.

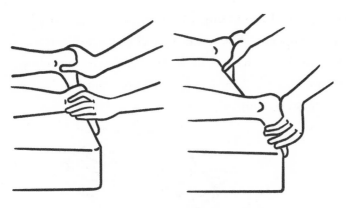

Different Handedness   Same Handedness

2) In doing a Short Circuit, the second operator should stand behind you, placing his hands on your shoulders next to your arms, if he is of the same handedness as you.

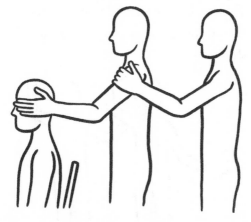

If of different handedness, he will have to stand with his back to you, reaching behind him. This cannot practically be done if you are standing, but if you sit down to work on the recipient while the second operator stands, then it can be done.

Personally, I would forget it in this second case and have the second operator hold onto the recipient's feet instead.

One thing that might be done is for the second operator to hold his hands near–not touching–your hands as you do the Short Circuit.

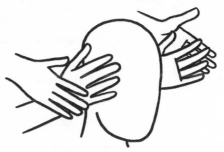

Be sure his negative hand is held over your negative hand, and his positive hand over your positive hand.

3) In Putting In, the second operator raises his negative hand as you are doing, but he places his positive hand on your negative shoulder.

4) In Drawing Out, the tandem methods outlined above for the Short Circuit and Putting In do not seem to have any value. Having a second operator hold the recipient's feet is however of marked effect in Drawing Out.

In all of these I have simply outlined the participation of a second operator. But there is no reason why there should not be a third, a fourth, or even twenty. I would advise caution, lest you overload the recipient with such high-voltage Magnetism, but in some cases–especially severe ones–it may be the solution. Some of the pioneers in Bio-Magnetic Therapy in the eighteenth century occasionally had every person in the household assist them in this way. But always be sure that the polarities do not get mixed and confused–especially if the people involved are of differing handedness.

LONG DISTANCE TREATMENT

Magnetism is not just universal–it is unitary. On the level of this basic life-force there are no divisions, just as an ocean is a unified body. Therefore space is no barrier in dealing with it. Odd as it may seem, you can treat people from a distance. My first experience with Magnetism was that of doing a long distance treatment. In that case it was only the distance from Ina's bathroom where I was to her living room, where Ina picked it up. But, as she said when I came back in the room: "If you can do it from twelve feet away you can do it from twelve thousand miles away." I was a believer, and since then have proved it to be so.

"The analogy between Absent Treatment and Wireless Telegraphy is almost perfect. If you assume that the Hertzian waves transmitted in wireless telegraphy represent the Healing Magnetism employed in Absent Treatment, then the analogy will be perfect, the ether in either case being the plastic medium between the two instruments, the vibration being the same, that is, as it passes through this plastic medium exercising a corresponding influence upon the organism of the patient.

"Absent Treatment is, therefore, not a figment of the imagination, not an illusion, not a mystical vagary, but is an application of known laws of physics to the healing of the body at a distance from the healer, its laws being the same as any other methods of healing" (Dr. A.S. Raleigh).

Rev. F.W. Sprague, one of the early and most successful of American Magnetic therapists, wrote in the same vein: "The nervous organism acts similar to a wireless telegraphic plant sending out these vital healing forces through the psychic ether and it acts upon that ether through the law of vibration similar to the action of Marconi's electric waves upon the atmosphere."

More technically, Mesmer, in his Memoir of 1799, said: "Thus, if a movement of the subtle substance is provoked within a body, there immediately occurs a similar movement in another sensitive to receiving it, whatever the distance between the two persons."

Magnetic therapists are not the only ones who affirm the reality of long distance treatment. Camille Flammarion, the French astronomer, wrote: "The action of one human being upon another, from a distance, is a scientific fact; it is as certain as the existence of Paris, of Napoleon, of Oxygen, or of Sirius.... There can be no doubt that our psychical form creates a movement, and the reverse may be analogous to what takes place on a telephone, where the receptive plate, which is identical with the plate at the other end, reconstructs the sonorous movement transmitted, not by means of sound, but by electricity. But these are only comparisons."

Bill Schul, in his book *The Psychic Frontiers of Medicine*, reports: "Several years ago Dr. Robert Miller, an Atlanta chemical engineer and former professor at Georgia Institute of Technology, determined to measure the influence of plant growth on an energy field generated by a healer at some distance away. He used a rotary electromechanical transducer and strip chart recorder in order to measure plant growth. Drs. Ambrose and Olga Worrall were asked to pray and send energy to the plants from their home in Baltimore, some six hundred miles away. During an eleven-hour period, the plants grew at the rate of 52.5 mils per hour—over eight hundred percent the normal rate!"

The Method

This is the method:

1) Be in a quiet place where you can be relaxed. Sit down if you wish.

2) If you know where the recipient is, face that direction. This is helpful, but not essential.

3) Fix firmly in your mind that you are going to treat that specific individual, that the Drawing Out or Putting In which

you will be doing will reach that person. There is no need to visualize the person, just to hold the thought-concept that the Magnetism is reaching his body. However, if it comes naturally to visualize, then do so.

4) If there is a specific body part that needs help you can feel (or visualize) that it is being effected. Or, you can just feel that the recipient in general is being effected.

5) Treat for as long as you like—no time limit need be observed here. But do wait seventy-two hours before treating again, except when it is an emergency where the results of non-treatment would be worse than any reactions that might be produced.

Some Pointers

Here are a couple of points from my experience with Long Distance treatment that might be useful to you.

I use either Putting In or Drawing Out according to which I feel will be most effective. Sometimes I try them both for a few minutes and then decide which to use. Though I usually think of the specific area(s) where help is needed, I can also just feel as though I am Putting In or Drawing Out in/from the entire body: the energy and going from me right to them. If it helps to think of a particular area where it will enter, that is all right, but I can just think it is reading the person directly from me.

Sometimes it is good to just think of the whole body, rather than thinking of a particular part, so the entire system of the recipient can be benefitted, including other areas that neither I nor the recipient may know need help—and might not receive benefit if I concentrated on just one part of the recipient's body.

I have no need to visualize the person, just position my hands, firmly set in my mind that the Magnetic current is going to the recipient, and let it flow. Every time, for me personally, I can actually feel the person's presence right away. I prefer to work with my eyes closed so nothing visual can distract me. As a result, I feel just as if the recipient is right in the room, in front of me, and I am feeling his vibrations (which is in actuality his personal Magnetism). Because of this impression of the recipient being present, no affirmation, visualization, or imagining is needed. This, I am sure, can be your experience with practice. I know this is real, because there is a big difference between imagining or remembering a person's presence and really feeling it. The memory or imagination of a burn, for example, is not the same thing as really getting burned. And the difference is just about as dramatic in working with the Long Distance method.

CHAPTER FOUR:

CANCER AND MENTAL ILLNESS

Cancer?

It is said that we all get cancer sometime in our life—even several times. But the body resists and destroys it before it is of any significant growth. Even in recognized cancer patients, what the medical profession terms "spontaneous remission" sometimes occurs. By that they mean that in some mysterious way the cancer has been dissolved. The "mysterious way" is not mysterious at all—it is simply the natural, self-healing powers within the body.

I don't feel that I can say it any better than Dr. A.S. Raleigh, so I will quote his views on the matter:

"The proper thing to do is to bring a current of Magnetism through the body and out through this cancer [by using the Drawing Out method].... Let this current of Magnetic force flowing from the body, stream out through the cancer, carrying away this waste product.... This cancerous tissue which is eating away and poisoning the sound tissue, must also be permeated with magnetism.....

"You must kill this cancerous state and remove this tissue in this Magnetic way.... Concentrate a strong current of vitality so as to intensely vitalize the part of the body, at the same time giving the food which will help to throw off this cancerous poison....

"Be very careful in doing this. If you make the slightest slip you are liable to take the cancer yourself, because you are really drawing those forces out into your negative hand; therefore, after you have given a treatment, be sure to concentrate your force very positively and make it flow out....

"Also, while treating a patient for cancer do not let any one else stay in the room; there is danger of giving it to others; also it is best not to treat another patient for another fifteen or twenty minutes after treating a cancerous patient, because there is danger of the evil Magnetism affecting the next patient, and the room should be fumigated with incense of a very powerful character, immediately after a treatment of that kind, so as to destroy the poison which is driven out of the system.....

"One thing we must call your attention to: Do not follow the practice of placing the positive hand over the cancer and directing the force inward [through the Putting In method].... What you want to do is not to drive the force into the cancer, but draw the poison out of the system through the cancer, as the cancer is the effort of Nature to eliminate this waste, and we should cooperate with this effort, work in conjunction with it, and by doing this we will be able to hasten the cure."

As has been said before, Bio-Magnetic Therapy increases and stimulates the natural self-curing force within the body. So nothing could be more appropriate to utilize in cases of cancer—and of benign tumors, as well. However, I personally would never rely on Bio-Magnetic Therapy alone if I had cancer or a tumor. I would consult a qualified physician. Further, I would read whatever I could find on the nutritional control of cancer. Especially I would make *How Not To Die* by Dr. Michael Greger my nutrition Bible.

Mental Illness?

If "only in a healthy body can you have a healthy mind," there is no reason why Bio-Magnetic Therapy could not be of help to mentally troubled or ill people just from the standpoint that it can assist the body in maintaining health. On my part, I am really convinced that a lot of mental aberration is really physical aberration, and modern psychiatry seems to agree– otherwise why should psychiatrists be medical doctors and not simply psychologists? Even more, I believe that confused polarity results in mental confusion and may even, if serious enough, produce "insane" behavior. Previously I have told my experience in having my own polarity confused. I believe that if a person underwent what I did–though to a much greater degree and for a prolonged time–he could not help but become "peculiar" from just the weirdness of feeling and mental confusion that he might experience. Often we hear of cases where a person has undergone a traumatic experience, and then developed mental problems. Emotional shock especially causes confusion–and even reversal–of polarity. Any person who has experienced a shock of any kind–physical or mental– should have their polarity checked and corrected. Accidents also produce confused polarity, as a rule. Anything that jolts the system either mentally or physically (since they cannot be separated) can upset the Magnetic flow in our bodies. Stubbing your toe or stumbling can confuse your polarity.

Not to suggest that teen-agers are crazy, but you may find that Bio-Magnetic Therapy can be of great help in those years when so much nervous instability and emotional growing pains manifest themselves.

The elderly also, who so often are labeled as senile or suffering from old age, may be found to simply have confused polarity.

I am certainly not suggesting that you start working with the mentally disturbed to the exclusion of qualified professional help for them; but I do think that Bio-Magnetic Therapy could certainly speed their recovery, and you should not hesitate to use it for their benefit.

CHAPTER FIVE:

INCREASING YOUR MAGNETISM

The more magnetic you are, the more efficiently and effectively you can apply Bio-Magnetic Therapy. So everyone who wants to seriously work with Magnetism should strive to be as magnetic as possible. The following are some ways in which I believe you can markedly enhance your magnetism.

Diet

The body tissues and nerves are the receptacles and instruments of Magnetism, and their condition can be either more or less conducive to Magnetism depending on their condition. The body is not just a magnet, it is an electrical magnet–we can even say it is a battery. And just as certain chemical solutions are needed to run a battery, so a certain body chemistry is needed for magnetic efficiency.

Magnetism is not electricity. Therefore, although electricity is all the same quality, no matter how it is generated, Magnetism varies. It carries with it the qualities of its source. The body is an energy extractor (much more impressive and efficient than an atomic reactor), and just as a loom can weave many types of thread into cloth that differs according to the type and origin of the thread, so the energy-magnetism of the body and mind is conditioned by food.

So I again strongly recommend Dr. Michael Greger's *How Not To Die*, as well as his *How Not To Diet*. You will find that a diet based on the principles of these two books will improve both your health and your Magnetism.

Copper rings

Strange as it may seem, the wearing of copper rings on the ring fingers can increase your Magnetism to a marked degree. The rings should not be just any kind, but a particular type. They should be formed from heavy copper wire (No. 10 gauge is the best). The ring for your positive hand should be formed of a copper wire fashioned into two circular loops, wound clockwise. The ring for your negative hand should be formed of a copper wire fashioned into three circular loops, wound counterclockwise.

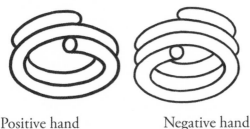

Positive hand   Negative hand

Why copper, and why the differing number of loops for the hands? I do not know. Any explanation I might give would only be an ignorant guess. What I do know is that every person

I have worked with has had the Magnetism of their hands increased by nearly one hundred percent by the wearing of these rings.

Someone who has a ring mandrel can make them for you if you know your ring size. The copper wire can be gotten from a hardware or electrical supply store in the form of "solid copper electrical wire" (you will need to remove the insulation). Some crafts and jeweler's supply stores sell the right kind of copper wire, as well. If you want a ring mandrel of your own you can no doubt get one from a jeweler's supply company.

You can either only wear the rings while working on people, or wear them all the time.

CHAPTER SIX:

Things That Decrease Or Unbalance Your Magnetism

Already we have discussed some things that decrease or interrupt the movement of Magnetism. But we should consider them a bit more.

Leather

Leather acts as an inhibitor of Magnetic flow–perhaps because it has an insulating property, or it retains some Magnetic field of its own, since it is the skin of a once-living animal. Anyhow, leather belts and shoes will certainly cut down the Magnetic flow of the operator in applying Bio-Magnetic Therapy. So when you work on someone, try to wear a non-leather belt and shoes (or none at all) during the time of treatment. The recipient, too, should remove his belt and shoes if they are leather.

Whether, then, a person should wear leather at all is a good question; since if it does inhibit Magnetic flow it cannot be good to wear leather all day long. This may be why the yogis of India prohibit leather, and not just from principles of non-violence.

Fabrics

As we have discussed before, the wearing of wool and silk hinders the flow of Magnetism. It has even been suggested by some researchers on Magnetism that wearing some types of synthetic materials is injurious to the health. If so, might it be because of the fabrics' effect on the body's Magnetism?

Jewelry

Since, as also discussed previously, metal jewelry inhibits Magnetic flow in therapy, there is good reason to suppose that such metal jewelry causes irregularity in the Magnetic circulation in the body at all times, and therefore may cause blockages, leaks, or low voltage in the body parts contacted–even through a layer or two of clothing.

Am I suggesting that you throw your jewelry away? Not at all; but I do suggest that once you have developed your Magnetic sensitivity, you test whether or not some pieces of your jewelry might not effect the circulation of Magnetism in your body.

Hypnotism

Hypnotism is very little understood, but it creates a static condition in the Magnetism that should be flowing evenly through your body. Any kind of induced trance state has a negative effect on you in the long run. I am talking about the old-fashioned form of hypnotism I grew up with, not the deep relaxation that is also sometimes called hypnotism. That is a different condition altogether and does not affect Magnetism.

Zone Therapy/Reflexology

The type of Zone Therapy (Reflexology) in which the operator puts heavy pressure on areas of the foot and pokes or gouges those areas, is extremely detrimental to the body's Magnetism, and throws off its normal circulation. The temporary relief given by such a system of Zone Therapy is bought at too dear a price.

Treatment With Magnets

It is a mistake to use magnets in therapy, because they interrupt the natural flow of the body's magnetism and often cause a static condition that inhibits or even stops the magnetic flow. The side effects of treatment with magnets is not worth it. Furthermore, the magnetism put out by a piece of metal or plastic is just not the same as the Magnetism of your body. And your body needs a force in total compatibility with it for efficient healing. Bio-Magnetic Therapy as given in this book supplies exactly that.

"Electric" Acupuncture

Traditional acupuncture is wonderful, and I recommend it. But acupuncture that sends an electrical current into the body through a probe or acupuncture needles can really wreak havoc with your Magnetism. I have had just one acupuncture treatment which involved electricity, and that was enough! The effect was drastic, and not worth the little benefit received. One person being treated in the enclosure just next to me began to faint after a few seconds of the treatment. No thanks.

Electric Shocks

If you get an electrical shock, have your polarity corrected immediately.

X-Rays

Sometimes we all have to get X-rayed. So when you do, right away have your polarity checked and corrected if need be, and Draw Out from the area that was x-rayed (If that area was worked on in less than seventy-two hours, then Draw Out for just three to five minutes).

Fluorescent Lights

Studies have shown that prolonged exposure to fluorescent lights can be detrimental to your health. Avoid all use of such lights whenever possible or use full-spectrum lights.

Kirilian Photography

There was once a great interest in this method of studying the subtle Magnetic radiations of the body. But it has been found that elements in the bone structure of the body can be damaged by such high frequency bombardment as is required for the production of the photographs.

Insecticides and Detergents

Insecticides adversely affect your body's Magnetism. Even more common a culprit is the detergent you use daily. The prolonged use of detergents in dishwashing, hand laundering, etc., can significantly inhibit the Magnetic flow within the hands. Since you "breathe in" your negative hand, and "breathe out" your positive hand, you can imagine the effect on your body of those channels being blocked! Many body soaps contain detergents, and some even advertise themselves as "detergent bars." Caution is needed here, too.

Comfrey

Mrs. Francis Nixon and her fellow-researchers have discovered that tea made from comfrey leaves causes a static condition in the Magnetism of the bones in the mouth, throat, and upper chest. Whether the comfrey root also has this effect is not yet known.

Nicotine and alcohol

Nicotine and alcohol wreak havoc with your body's Magnetism. They should never be taken into your body. Tobacco and alcoholic beverages are poisonous drugs that damage the body and mind. Those who smoke or drink are filled with toxins and deranged Magnetism. That includes the light users of those substances, as well as the heavy users. NEVER should they attempt to apply Bio-Magnetic Therapy, for they will transfer the negative Magnetism in their bodies to the recipient's body. And they will be much harder to work on as recipients. I would almost never Draw Out from smokers or drinkers, or apply the Short Circuit on them. The Body Sweep and Putting In are the only processes I would use.

Personal Associations

People and places can be negative and destructive to your health. Mark them out and stay away. Some people are energy vampires. Certain jobs are negative and harm health. Negative energy infects people just as much as germs. Beware.

Dr. Raleigh said: "Many people are made sick because of the company they keep, [even] because of their families.... Do not have disagreeable people around if you would maintain a state of health, because they will necessarily disturb your emotional states and antagonize the entire being. The result will be a state of discord which must express itself in a corresponding disease.

"Also, it must be borne in mind that if a person within himself leads a life of antagonism, a life of bitterness, of hatred—maintains a discordant condition within his own being—then he is sinning against the Law of Harmony, the Law of Peace. The result is, he is establishing that state of discord which must express itself in corresponding diseases, and so sickness is really the punishment for sins; it is the consequences which a life of discord brings, and sickness can never be permanently cured except by the permanent removal of the causes, namely, the state of discord. Harmony must be produced within the very being before he can be brought into a state of permanent health.

"If the old emotions continue to go on, if the person continues to be swayed by them, he will continue to generate those poisons without any cessation and consequently, he will have to continue to neutralize those poisons, and continue to have them cured and removed, because just as long as the poisoning goes on, just so long will there be a job for the doctor, and it will continue just as long as those emotions are continued."

Above all, watch what you feed your mind through books, conversations and entertainment. Negative thoughts and habits are subtle poison that they kill your inner being, which is the real you.

Sleeping

I really don't know where to put this bit of information, so it will have to go here.

Never sleep with your head to the north—that is, with your feet to the south and your head at the north. This tends to reverse and confuse your polarity. So get a good compass and check where you sleep, and take it with you when you travel.

Any other direction for sleeping is fine. But sleeping with your feet toward the north and your head at the south is the most beneficial for health, according to some. This is my favorite, as well. You do not need to sleep with your head at exact south, east, or west, but pretty much so.

I have seen several people relieved of nervous problems and unexplained tension, just by shifting their sleeping position.

People who sleep together should make sure they are not sleeping with their positive or negative sides next to each other.

This creates Magnetic conflict. I have known married couples who eliminated conflicts between themselves by changing the sides of the bed they slept on.

CHAPTER SEVEN:

OVERCOMING A STATIC CONDITION

You may find that for some unknown reason your own Magnetism will just slow down in its flow to a marked degree (of course, it does not really stop altogether), and you have difficulty in applying Bio-Magnetic Therapy to others.

Sometimes this is our own Magnetic system warning us that we are not in good enough physical condition to apply Magnetism just at that time. It is a safety device. So if, after trying the things I am going to suggest in this chapter, your Magnetism is still in a (nearly) static condition, then accept it and take off a few days until you find your Magnetism flowing again normally.

As soon as you get into the static condition, have your polarity checked. This may be the problem. But if your polarity is just fine but weak, try these three following methods (one may be sufficient).

Vitalization Stance

Remove your shoes. Stand upright and raise your arms out and level with your shoulders so you are standing in the form of a Cross. Stand so the fingers of your positive hand are pointing South and the fingers of your negative hand are pointing North.

The palm of your positive hand should be turned down, and the palm of your negative hand should be turned up. Then cup your hands and fingers so the fingertips are pointing up (negative hand) and down (positive hand).

Stand in this way, relaxed for a few minutes, and be attentive to the feelings of Magnetic flow in your hands. It is important to remain as relaxed as possible when doing this. If your arms get tired, stop for a while and then resume the Stance. Three to five minutes should be enough, but if after ten or fifteen minutes there is no increase in your Magnetic flow, then do the next method.

Salt and Soda Bath

One of the best Magnetic therapists of the nineteenth and early twentieth century was Colonel Olcott, co-founder of the Theosophical Society. The cures he worked in Ceylon and India were astonishing to all (including himself, at first). He writes in his memoirs, *Old Diary Leaves*, that at times he, too, experienced a static condition in his Magnetism. At such times, when he was in Ceylon, he would go for a swim in the ocean. Emerging from the ocean, he would find himself revitalized and ready to go back to more treatment.

Mrs. Francis Nixon, in her admirable work on bioenergies, discovered that a bath in a solution of sea salt and soda was able to correct static conditions in the Magnetism.

Here is how to do it: Dissolve one pound of sea salt (most health food stores carry it—but be sure there are no additives) and one pound of baking soda in a bathtub of lukewarm water not hotter than 90-98 degrees. Submerge your whole body in this solution, and soak for about ten minutes, immersing your head, as well, for short intervals. Be sure your shoulders are completely submerged. Have a similar solution in a water glass, and rinse your mouth out with it a few times, as well. Only you who are taking the bath should stir the salt and soda into the water with your own hands.

Feet In Earth

Something that is very helpful to the increase and balance of Magnetism (even if your Magnetic flow is all right) is to go outside in the early morning just before dawn, dig out a small cavity and stand in it, facing toward the rising sun, covering your feet back up with the earth. Stand there as the sun rises (you might try the Vitalization Stance while doing this).

Another good practice is to walk barefoot on the dew and grass at sunrise.

CHAPTER EIGHT:

Pass It On

D id you know that at one time in this country Magnetic healing was so widespread and popular that even the most sober practitioners predicted that it would replace all other forms of treatment in a few decades? Tens of thousands flocked to Dr. Weltmer's Institute in Nevada, Missouri, where it was common to treat four hundred people a day. And that was only one center.

Today, Bio-Magnetic Therapy is virtually unknown.

What happened?

The same thing that happened to the great Magnetic healing movement of Anton Mesmer: greed and professionalism. People opened up offices and clinics, kept their methods secret (or taught them for a high price to students sworn to secrecy, who in their turn did the same), and charged people for what the patients or their friends and family members could have done themselves. I have a book that claims to be a guide for Magnetic healers. It is one hundred and twenty-five pages long, but only a little over five pages contain instruction, and that instruction is so poorly and sketchily given that no one could apply it. Obviously it was the author's intention to make money on the book yet not tell would-be competitors how to really do it. This self-seeking mentality has caused a great knowledge to almost be lost. And it certainly is virtually unknown.

Dr. Mesmer lamented: "The advantages and the singular nature of this system was responsible, some years ago, for the eagerness of the public to grasp the first hopes which I held out; and it is by perverting them that envy, presumption and incredulity have in a very short space of time succeeded in relegating them to the status of illusions, causing them to fall into oblivion."

Even worse—because it is deception—some people use these natural principles of healing, but dress them up with the titles of "psychic healing" or "spiritual healing," while touting their "unique gift from God," even though they know that all their admirers and financial supporters can do the same as they. Ina Bryant was hated by many people who claimed to heal by "laying on of hands" because her book showed how they really healed.

I have spent a great deal of time and money researching and writing this book. Not one penny from this book will ever come to me from this effort. All profit from this book will go into a fund to print more books to help others. But I would like to ask a "profit" from you: apply these principles in your own life and pass it on. Help others. Teach them these methods. Get more copies of this little book and spread the word around. The good you do will benefit both you and me, for our neighbor is ourself, and when one is benefited we all gain from it.

At the end of his life, Mesmer wrote: "More important than the obstacles which have been thrown in my way, I have believed it necessary to progress to publish my ideas. I voluntarily surrender my theory to criticism, declaring that I have neither the time nor the desire to reply to it. I have nothing to say to those who are incapable of crediting me with integrity or generosity, and who cannot substitute anything better for that of mine which they seek to destroy.

"I would regard with pleasure any better inspirations which might bring forth sounder, more enlightened principles–some talent better understood than mine, which might discover new facts and perhaps make my doctrine even more beneficial by new conceptions and work. In brief, I wish that someone might go further than I have gone....

"Although I am rather advanced in years, I wish to dedicate my remaining life to the sole practice of a method that I have discovered to be eminently useful in the preservation of my fellowman."

This book is ended. But I hope it is only the beginning for you and for many others.

DID YOU ENJOY
READING THIS BOOK?

Thank you for reading *Bio-Magnetic Therapy*. If you enjoyed it, please consider telling your friends or posting a short review at Amazon.com, Goodreads, or the online site of your choice.

Word of mouth is an author's best friend and much appreciated

GET YOUR FREE MEDITATION GUIDE

Sign up for the Light of the Spirit Newsletter and get
Learn How to Meditate Effectively.

Get free updates: newsletters, blog posts, and podcasts, plus
exclusive content from Light of the Spirit Monastery.

Visit: https://ocoy.org/signup

ABOUT THE AUTHOR

Swami Nirmalananda Giri (Abbot George Burke) is the founder and director of the Light of the Spirit Monastery (Atma Jyoti Ashram) in Cedar Crest, New Mexico, USA.

In his many pilgrimages to India, he had the opportunity of meeting some of India's greatest spiritual figures, including Swami Sivananda of Rishikesh and Anandamayi Ma. During his first trip to India he was made a member of the ancient Swami Order by Swami Vidyananda Giri, a direct disciple of Paramhansa Yogananda, who had himself been given sannyas by the Shankaracharya of Puri, Jagadguru Bharati Krishna Tirtha.

In the United States he also encountered various Christian saints, including Saint John Maximovich of San Francisco and Saint Philaret Voznesensky of New York. He was ordained in the Liberal Catholic Church (International) to the priesthood on January 25, 1974, and consecrated a bishop on August 23, 1975.

For many years Swami Nirmalananda has researched the identity of Jesus Christ and his teachings with India and Sanatana Dharma, including Yoga. It is his conclusion that Jesus lived in India for most of his life, and was a yogi and Sanatana Dharma missionary to the West. After his resurrection he returned to India and lived the rest of his life in the Himalayas.

He has written extensively on these and other topics, many of which are posted at OCOY.org.

ATMA JYOTI ASHRAM
(LIGHT OF THE SPIRIT MONASTERY)

Atma Jyoti Ashram (Light of the Spirit Monastery) is a monastic community for those men who seek direct experience of the Spirit through yoga meditation, traditional yogic discipline, Sanatana Dharma and the life of the sannyasi in the tradition of the Order of Shankara. Our lineage is in the Giri branch of the Order.

The public outreach of the monastery is through its website, OCOY.org (Original Christianity and Original Yoga). There you will find many articles on Original Christianity and Original Yoga, including *The Christ of India*. *Foundations of Yoga* and *How to Be a Yogi* are practical guides for anyone seriously interested in living the Yoga Life.

You will also discover many other articles on leading an effective spiritual life, including *Soham Yoga: The Yoga of the Self* and *Spiritual Benefits of a Vegetarian Diet*, as well as the "Dharma for Awakening" series—in-depth commentaries on these spiritual classics: the Bhagavad Gita, the Upanishads, the Dhammapada, the Tao Teh King and more.

You can listen to podcasts by Swami Nirmalananda on meditation, the Yoga Life, and remarkable spiritual people he has met in India and elsewhere, at http://ocoy.org/podcasts/

READING FOR AWAKENING

Light of the Spirit Press presents books on spiritual wisdom and Original Christianity and Original Yoga. From our "Dharma for Awakening" series (practical commentaries on the world's scriptures) to books on how to meditate and live a successful spiritual life, you will find books that are informative, helpful, and even entertaining.

Light of the Spirit Press is the publishing house of Light of the Spirit Monastery (Atma Jyoti Ashram) in Cedar Crest, New Mexico, USA. Our books feature the writings of the founder and director of the monastery, Swami Nirmalananda Giri (Abbot George Burke) which are also found on the monastery's website, OCOY.org.

We invite you to explore our publications in the following pages.

Find out more about our publications at
lightofthespiritpress.com

BOOKS ON MEDITATION

Soham Yoga
The Yoga of the Self

A complete and in-depth guide to effective meditation and the life that supports it, this important book explains with clarity and insight what real yoga is, and why and how to practice Soham Yoga meditation.

Discovered centuries ago by the Nath yogis, this simple and classic approach to self-realization has no "secrets," requires no "initiation," and is easily accessible to the serious modern yogi.

Includes helpful, practical advice on leading an effective spiritual life and many Illuminating quotes on Soham from Indian scriptures and great yogis.

"This book is a complete spiritual path." –Arnold Van Wie

Light of Soham
The Life and Teachings of Sri Gajanana Maharaj of Nashik

Gajanan Murlidhar Gupte, later known as Gajanana Maharaj, led an unassuming life, to all appearances a normal unmarried man of contemporary society. Crediting his personal transformation to the practice of the Soham mantra, he freely shared this practice with a small number of disciples, whom he simply called his friends. Strictly avoiding the trap of gurudom, he insisted that his friends be self-reliant and not be dependent on him for their spiritual progress. Yet he was uniquely able to assist them in their inner development.

The Inspired Wisdom of Gajanana Maharaj
A Practical Commentary on Leading an Effectual Spiritual Life

Presents the teachings and sayings of the great twentieth-century Soham yogi Gajanana Maharaj, with a commentary by Swami Nirmalananda.

The author writes: "In reading about Gajanana Maharaj I encountered a holy personality that eclipsed all others for me. In his words I found a unique wisdom that altered my perspective on what yoga, yogis, and gurus should be.

"But I realized that through no fault of their own, many Western readers need a clarification and expansion of Maharaj's meaning to get the right understanding of his words. This commentary is meant to help my friends who, like me have found his words 'a light in the darkness.'"

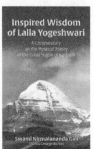

Inspired Wisdom of Lalla Yogeshwari
A Commentary on the Mystical Poetry of the Great Yogini of Kashmir

Lalla Yogeshwari was a great fourteenth-century yogini and wandering ascetic of Kashmir, whose mystic poetry were the earliest compositions in the Kashmiri language. She was in the tradition of the Nath Yogi Sampradaya whose meditation practice is that of Soham Sadhana: the joining of the mental repetition of Soham Mantra with the natural breath.

Swami Nirmalananda's commentary mines the treasures of Lalleshwari's mystic poems and presents his reflections in an easily intelligible fashion for those wishing to put these priceless teachings on the path of yogic self-transformation into practice.

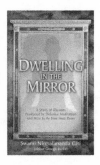

Dwelling in the Mirror
*A Study of Illusions Produced By Delusive Meditation
And How to Be Free from Them*

Swami Nirmalananda says of this book:

"Over and over people have mistaken trivial and pathological conditions for enlightenment, written books, given seminars and gained a devoted following.

"Most of these unfortunate people were completely unreachable with reason. Yet there are those who can have an experience and realize that it really cannot be real, but a vagary of their mind. Some may not understand that on their own, but can be shown by others the truth about it. For them and those that may one day be in danger of meditation-produced delusions I have written this brief study."

Books on Yoga & Spiritual Life

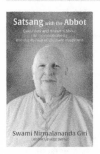

Satsang with the Abbot
Questions and Answers about Life, Spiritual Liberty, and the Pursuit of Ultimate Happiness

The questions in this book range from the most sublime to the most practical. "How can I attain samadhi?" "I am married with children. How can I lead a spiritual life?" "What is Self-realization?" "How important is belief in karma and reincarnation?"

In Swami Nirmalananda's replies to these questions the reader will discover common sense, helpful information, and a guiding light for their journey through and beyond the forest of cliches, contradictions, and confusion of yoga, Hinduism, Christianity, and metaphysical thought.

Foundations of Yoga
Ten Important Principles Every Meditator Should Know

An introduction to the important foundation principles of Patanjali's Yoga: Yama and Niyama

Yama and Niyama are often called the Ten Commandments of Yoga, but they have nothing to do with the ideas of sin and virtue or good and evil as dictated by some cosmic potentate. Rather they are determined by a thoroughly practical, pragmatic basis: that which strengthens and facilitates our yoga practice should be observed and that which weakens or hinders it should be avoided.

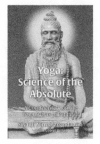

Yoga: Science of the Absolute
A Commentary on the Yoga Sutras of Patanjali

The Yoga Sutras of Patanjali is the most authoritative text on Yoga as a practice. It is also known as the Yoga Darshana because it is the fundamental text of Yoga as a philosophy.

In this commentary, Swami Nirmalananda draws on the age-long tradition regarding this essential text, including the commentaries of Vyasa and Shankara, the most highly regarded writers on Indian philosophy and practice, as well as I. K. Taimni and other authoritative commentators, and adds his own ideas based on half a century of study and practice. Serious students of yoga will find this an essential addition to their spiritual studies.

The Benefits of Brahmacharya
A Collection of Writings About the Spiritual, Mental, and Physical Benefits of Continence

"Brahmacharya is the basis for morality. It is the basis for eternal life. It is a spring flower that exhales immortality from its petals." Swami Sivananda

This collection of articles from a variety of authorities including Mahatma Gandhi, Sri Ramakrishna, Swami Vivekananda, Swamis Sivananda and Chidananda of the Divine Life Society, Swami Nirmalananda, and medical experts, presents many facets of brahmacharya and will prove of immense value to all who wish to grow spiritually.

Living the Yoga Life
Perspectives on Yoga

"Dive deep; otherwise you cannot get the gems at the bottom of the ocean. You cannot pick up the gems if you only float on the surface." Sri Ramakrishna

In *Living the Yoga Life* Swami Nirmalananda shares the gems he has found from a lifetime of "diving deep." This collection of reflections and short essays addresses the key concepts of yoga philosophy that are so easy to take for granted. Never content with the accepted cliches about yoga sadhana, the yoga life, the place of a guru, the nature of Brahman and our unity with It, Swami Nirmalananda's insights on these and other facets of the yoga life will inspire, provoke, enlighten, and even entertain.

Spiritual Benefits of a Vegetarian Diet

The health benefits of a vegetarian diet are well known, as are the ethical aspects. But the spiritual advantages should be studied by anyone involved in meditation, yoga, or any type of spiritual practice.

Diet is a crucial aspect of emotional, intellectual, and spiritual development as well. For diet and consciousness are interrelated, and purity of diet is an effective aid to purity and clarity of consciousness.

The major thing to keep in mind when considering the subject of vegetarianism is its relevancy in relation to our explorations of consciousness. We need only ask: Does it facilitate my spiritual growth–the development and expansion of my consciousness? The answer is Yes.

BOOKS ON THE SACRED SCRIPTURES OF INDIA

The Bhagavad Gita for Awakening
A Practical Commentary for Leading a Successful Spiritual Life

Drawing from the teachings of Sri Ramakrishna, Jesus, Paramhansa Yogananda, Ramana Maharshi, Swami Vivekananda, Swami Sivananda of Rishikesh, Papa Ramdas, and other spiritual masters and teachers, as well as his own experiences, Swami Nirmalananda illustrates the teachings of the Gita with stories which make the teachings of Krishna in the Gita vibrant and living.

From *Publisher's Weekly*: "[The author] enthusiastically explores the story as a means for knowing oneself, the cosmos, and one's calling within it. His plainspoken insights often distill complex lessons with simplicity and sagacity. Those with a deep interest in the Gita will find much wisdom here."

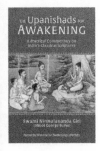

The Upanishads for Awakening
A Practical Commentary on India's Classical Scriptures

The sacred scriptures of India are vast. Yet they are only different ways of seeing the same thing, the One Thing which makes them both valid and ultimately harmonious. That unifying subject is Brahman: God the Absolute, beyond and besides whom there is no "other" whatsoever. The thirteen major Upanishads are the fountainhead of all expositions of Brahman.

Swami Nirmalananda Giri illumines the Upanishads' practical value for spiritual seekers from the unique perspective of a lifetime of study and practice of both Eastern and Western spirituality.

The Bhagavad Gita–The Song of God

Often called the "Bible" of Hinduism, the Bhagavad Gita is found in households throughout India and has been translated into every major language of the world. Literally billions of copies have been handwritten or printed.

The clarity of this translation by Swami Nirmalananda makes for easy reading, while the rich content makes this the ideal "study" Gita. As the original Sanskrit language is so rich, often there are several accurate translations for the same word, which are noted in the text, giving the spiritual student the needed understanding of the fullness of the Gita.

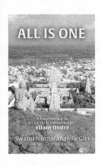

All Is One
A Commentary On Sri Vaiyai R. Subramanian's Ellam Ondre

"I you want moksha, read and practice the instructions in *Ellam Ondre*."
Ramana Maharshi

Swami Nirmalananda's insightful commentary brings even further light to Ellam Ondre's refreshing perspective on what Unity signifies, and the path to its realization.

Written in the colorful and well-informed style typical of his other commentaries, it is a timely and important contribution to Advaitic literature that explains Unity as the fruit of yoga sadhana, rather than mere wishful thinking or some vague intellectual gymnastic, as is so commonly taught by the modern "Advaita gurus."

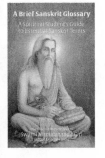

A Brief Sanskrit Glossary
A Spiritual Student's Guide to Essential Sanskrit Terms

This Sanskrit glossary contains full translations and explanations of hundreds of the most commonly used spiritual Sanskrit terms, and will help students of the Bhagavad Gita, the Upanishads, the Yoga Sutras of Patanjali, and other Indian scriptures and philosophical works to expand their vocabularies to include the Sanskrit terms contained in these, and gain a fuller understanding in their studies.

Books on Original Christianity

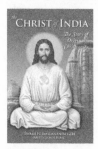

The Christ of India
The Story of Original Christianity

"Original Christianity" is the teaching of both Jesus and his Apostle Saint Thomas in India. Although it was new to the Mediterranean world, it was really the classical, traditional teachings of the rishis of India that even today comprise the Eternal Dharma, that goes far beyond religion into realization.

In *The Christ of India* Swami Nirmalananda presents what those ancient teachings are, as well as the growing evidence that Jesus spent much of his "Lost Years" in India and Tibet. This is also the story of how the original teachings of Jesus and Saint Thomas thrived in India for centuries before the coming of the European colonialists.

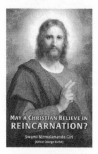

May a Christian Believe in Reincarnation?

Discover the real and surprising history of reincarnation and Christianity.

A growing number of people are open to the subject of past lives, and the belief in rebirth–reincarnation, metempsychosis, or transmigration–is commonplace. It often thought that belief in reincarnation and Christianity are incompatible. But is this really true? May a Christian believe in reincarnation? The answer may surprise you.

"Those needing evidence that a belief in reincarnation is in accordance with teachings of the Christ need look no further: Plainly laid out and explained in an intelligent manner from one who has spent his life on a Christ-like path of renunciation and prayer/meditation."—*Christopher T. Cook*

The Unknown Lives of Jesus and Mary
Compiled from Ancient Records and Mystical Revelations

"There are also many other things which Jesus did, the which, if they should be written every one, I suppose that even the world itself could not contain the books that should be written." (Gospel of Saint John, final verse)

You can discover much of those "many other things" in this unique compilation of ancient records and mystical revelations, which includes historical records of the lives of Jesus Christ and his Mother Mary that have been accepted and used by the Church since apostolic times. This treasury of little-known stories of Jesus' life will broaden the reader's understanding of what Christianity really was in its original form.

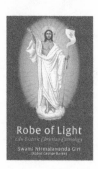

Robe of Light
An Esoteric Christian Cosmology

In *Robe of Light* Swami Nirmalananda explores the whys and wherefores of the mystery of creation. From the emanation of the worlds from the very Being of God, to the evolution of the souls to their ultimate destiny as perfected Sons of God, the ideal progression of creation is described. Since the rebellion of Lucifer and the fall of Adam and Eve from Paradise flawed the normal plan of evolution, a restoration was necessary. How this came about is the prime subject of this insightful study.

Moreover, what this means to aspirants for spiritual perfection is expounded, with a compelling knowledge of the scriptures and of the mystical traditions of East and West.

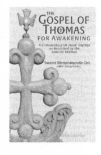

The Gospel of Thomas for Awakening
A Commentary on Jesus' Sayings as Recorded by the Apostle Thomas

When the Apostles dispersed to the various area of the world, Thomas travelled to India, where evidence shows Jesus spent his Lost Years, and which had been the source of the wisdom which he had brought to the "West."

The Christ that Saint Thomas quotes in this ancient text is quite different than the Christ presented by popular Christianity. Through his unique experience and study with both Christianity and Indian religion, Swami Nirmalananda clarifies the sometimes enigmatic sayings of Jesus in an informative and inspiring way.

The Odes of Solomon for Awakening
A Commentary on the Mystical Wisdom of the Earliest Christian Hymns and Poems

The Odes of Solomon is the earliest Christian hymn-book, and therefore one of the most important early Christian documents. Since they are mystical and esoteric, they teach and express the classical and universal mystical truths of Christianity, revealing a Christian perspective quite different than that of "Churchianity," and present the path of Christhood that all Christians are called to.

"Fresh and soothing, these 41 poems and hymns are beyond delightful! I deeply appreciate Abbot George Burke's useful and illuminating insight and find myself spiritually re-animated." John Lawhn

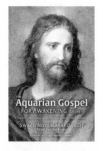

The Aquarian Gospel for Awakening (2 Volumes)
A Practical Commentary on Levi Dowling's Classic Life of Jesus Christ

Written in 1908 by the American mystic Levi Dowling, The Aquarian Gospel of Jesus the Christ answers many questions about Jesus' life that the Bible doesn't address. Dowling presents a universal message found at the heart of all valid religions, a broad vision of love and wisdom that will ring true with Christians who are attracted to Christ but put off by the narrow views of the tradition that has been given his name.

Swami Nirmalananda's commentary is a treasure-house of knowledge and insight that even further expands Dowling's vision of the true Christ and his message.

Wandering With The Cherubim
A Commentary on the Mystical Verse of Angelus Silesius–The Cherubinic Wanderer"

Johannes Scheffler, who wrote under the name Angelus Silesius, was a mystic and a poet. In his most famous book, "The Cherubinic Wanderer," he expressed his mystical vision.

Swami Nirmalananda reveals the timelessness of his mystical teachings and The Cherubinic Wanderer's practical value for spiritual seekers. He does this in an easily intelligible fashion for those wishing to put those priceless teachings into practice.

"Set yourself on the journey of this mystical poetry made accessible through this very beautifully commentated text. It is text that submerges one in the philosophical context of the Advaita notion of Non Duality. Swami Nirmalananda's commentary is indispensable in understanding higher philosophical ideas."–Savitri

BOOKS ON BUDDHISM & TAOISM

The Dhammapada for Awakening
A Commentary on Buddha's Practical Wisdom

Swami Nirmalananda's commentary on this classic Buddhist scripture explores the Buddha's answers to the urgent questions, such as "How can I find find lasting peace, happiness and fulfillment that seems so elusive?" and "What can I do to avoid many of the miseries big and small that afflict all of us?" Drawing on his personal experience and on parallels in Hinduism and Christianity, the author sheds new light on the Buddha's eternal wisdom.

"Swami Nirmalananda's commentary is well crafted and stacked with anecdotes and humor.I found it to be entertaining as well as illuminating, and have come to consider it a guide to daily living." –Rev. Gerry Nangle

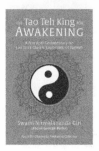

The Tao Teh King for Awakening
A Practical Commentary on Lao Tzu's Classic Exposition of Taoism

"The Tao does all things, yet our interior disposition determines our success or failure in coming to knowledge of the unknowable Tao."

Lao Tzu's classic writing, the Tao Teh King, has fascinated scholars and seekers for centuries. His presentation of the Tao which is the Eternal Reality, and the Way of the Sage that is the path to the realization of and dwelling in this Reality is illuminating, but its deeper meanings and practical applications remain obscure to many, especially in the West.

Swami Nirmalananda offers a commentary that makes the treasures of Lao Tzu's teachings accessible and applicable for the sincere seeker.

More Titles
The Four Gospels for Awakening

Light on the Path for Awakening

How to Read the Tarot

Light from Eternal Lamps

Vivekachudamani: The Crest Jewel of Discrimination for Awakening

Bio-Magnetic Therapy: Healing in Your Hands

Sanatana Dharma: The Eternal Religion

Made in the USA
Coppell, TX
26 September 2024

37753944R00069